Higher

Biology
revision notes

✗ **Andrew Morton** ✗

Text © 2003 Andrew Morton
Design and layout © 2003 Leckie & Leckie Ltd
Cover image © Caleb Rutherford and Photodisc/Getty Images

10/080208

ISBN 978-1-898890-18-8

Published by

Leckie & Leckie Ltd, 3rd Floor, 4 Queen Street, Edinburgh EH2 1JE
tel. 0131 220 6831 fax. 0131 225 9987
enquiries@leckieandleckie.co.uk   www.leckieandleckie.co.uk

Edited by
Priscilla Sharland and Frances McDonald

Special thanks to
Merlyn Gudgeon (illustration) and Caleb Rutherford (cover design)

A CIP Catalogue record for this book is available from the British Library.

Leckie & Leckie Ltd is a division of Huveaux plc.

CONTENTS

INTRODUCTION

This textbook is designed to cover the whole of the SQA National Qualification: **Higher Biology**.

The 160-hour course is divided into three units.
To obtain a pass in Higher Biology you must, for each unit, pass a short unit test of 40 marks (pass mark 26). You must also write up **one** practical investigation which will be marked by your teacher or lecturer.

In addition, you must pass a $2\frac{1}{2}$ hour course examination of 130 marks, which is offered by the SQA in May of each year. Passes are graded A, B, C and D.

The course examination consists of **three** sections:
Section A   Thirty multiple-choice questions for 30 marks
Section B   Around 70 short-answer questions for 80 marks
Section C   Two extended-answer questions of 10 marks each, from a choice of four.

 A companion question book, *Questions in Higher Biology*, is written by the same author and is published by Leckie & Leckie. This text contains over 300 questions and a simplified syllabus summary.

Note that words which are likely to be examined appear in **bold** type the first time they appear in the text. Many of these key words are also listed in *Questions in Higher Biology*, each with a simple definition.

UNIT ONE — CELL BIOLOGY

This 40-hour unit contains information on cell structure and function, cell membranes and membrane transport, photosynthesis, respiration, DNA structure and replication, protein synthesis, viruses and cell defence mechanisms.

Cell structure and function

Living things are made of cells. Some organisms are composed of only one cell and are said to be **unicellular**. Others, like ourselves, are **multicellular**. Most cells are so small that they can only be seen under the microscope. All cells contain a fluid **cytoplasm** surrounded by a membrane called the **plasma membrane**. Under very powerful electron microscopes it is possible to see many tiny structures suspended in the cytoplasm. These tiny structures, called **organelles**, carry out the chemical processes which maintain the cells and hence the organisms to which they belong. These chemical processes are called the cell's **metabolism** and many of these metabolic reactions are catalysed by **enzymes**. A series of such reactions is referred to as a **metabolic pathway**.

A typical animal cell (as seen under an electron microscope)
The diagram is magnified 2000x. The cell measures 50 micrometres. One micrometre (1 μm) is a thousandth of a millimetre, or 10^{-6} m.

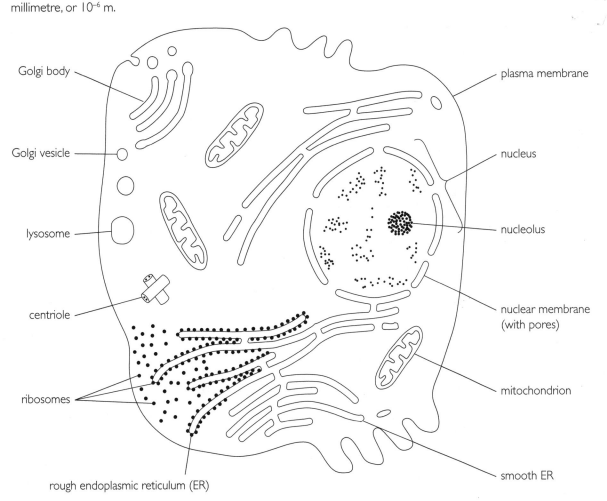

A typical plant cell (as seen under an electron microscope) The diagram is magnified 1500x.
What is the actual size of the mitochondria shown? (*The answer is at the back of the book.*)
Note that not all plant cells contain chloroplasts and vacuoles, but all are surrounded by a cell wall.

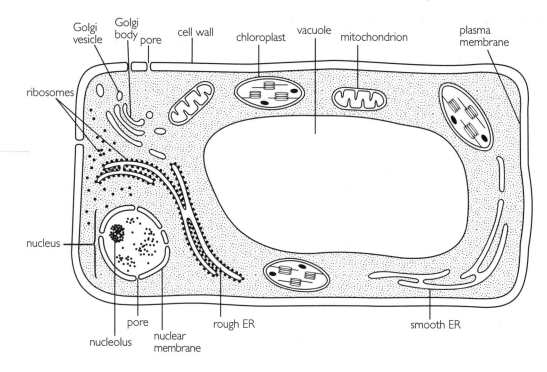

Organelle	Brief description of its function (what it does)
nucleus	contains DNA which acts as blueprint for the manufacture of proteins
nucleolus	involved in the synthesis of RNA and ribosomes
mitochondrion	site of production of energy-rich ATP by aerobic respiration
Golgi body	packaging of complex molecules for secretion by the cell
Golgi vesicle	small sac to enclose and transport complex molecules
rough endoplasmic reticulum (ER)	sheets of membrane covered in ribosomes and involved in the synthesis and transport of proteins for export from the cell
smooth ER	sheets of membranes with no ribosomes, involved in the synthesis and transport of lipids
ribosomes	found on the ER and free in the cytoplasm, they are the site of protein synthesis
centrioles	two cylindrical structures present only in animal cells and involved in the formation of the spindle fibres during mitosis and meiosis. (*See page 21.*)
lysosome	a sac, derived from Golgi vesicles, which contains digestive enzymes
chloroplast	found only in plant cells; contains the green pigment chlorophyll to trap light energy for the process of photosynthesis
vacuole	found in many plant cells; a sac containing water with dissolved substances. Contributes to cell turgor (firmness), and sometimes contains pigments which give colour to, for example, petals
cell wall	made of cellulose, a carbohydrate, it gives strength and support to plant cells. Is freely permeable, i.e. it allows substances to pass through it with ease

Cell variety

Cells vary enormously in size, shape and function. Single-celled organisms are composed of only one cell. However, multicellular animals and plants contain numerous types of specialised cells. Groups of similar cells working together to perform a particular function make up what is known as a **tissue**.

Below are some examples of unicellular organisms and specialised cells of multicellular organisms.

Unicellular organisms (Protists)

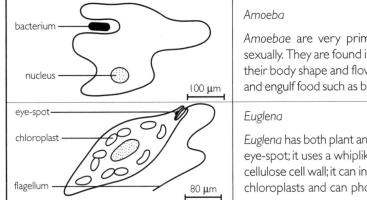

bacterium nucleus 100 μm	*Amoeba* Amoebae are very primitive organisms which do not reproduce sexually. They are found in water and in the soil and move by changing their body shape and flowing over surfaces. *Amoebae* can flow round and engulf food such as bacteria. This process is called **phagocytosis**.
eye-spot chloroplast flagellum 80 μm	*Euglena* *Euglena* has both plant and animal characteristics. It has a light sensitive eye-spot; it uses a whiplike flagellum to swim through water; it has no cellulose cell wall; it can ingest food by phagocytosis; but it also contains chloroplasts and can photosynthesise.

Specialised cells of multicellular organisms

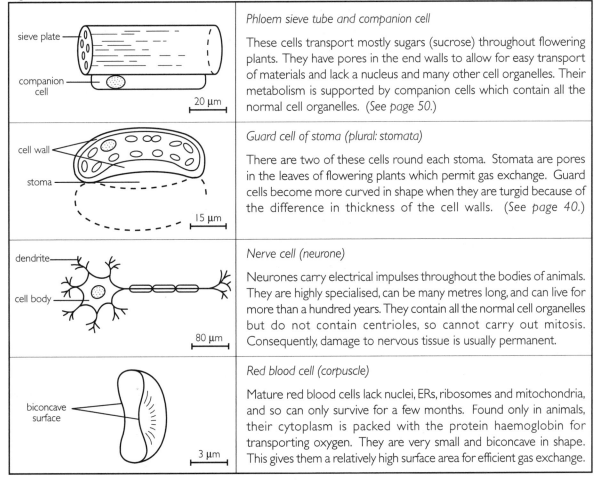

sieve plate companion cell 20 μm	*Phloem sieve tube and companion cell* These cells transport mostly sugars (sucrose) throughout flowering plants. They have pores in the end walls to allow for easy transport of materials and lack a nucleus and many other cell organelles. Their metabolism is supported by companion cells which contain all the normal cell organelles. (*See page 50.*)
cell wall stoma 15 μm	*Guard cell of stoma (plural: stomata)* There are two of these cells round each stoma. Stomata are pores in the leaves of flowering plants which permit gas exchange. Guard cells become more curved in shape when they are turgid because of the difference in thickness of the cell walls. (*See page 40.*)
dendrite cell body 80 μm	*Nerve cell (neurone)* Neurones carry electrical impulses throughout the bodies of animals. They are highly specialised, can be many metres long, and can live for more than a hundred years. They contain all the normal cell organelles but do not contain centrioles, so cannot carry out mitosis. Consequently, damage to nervous tissue is usually permanent.
biconcave surface 3 μm	*Red blood cell (corpuscle)* Mature red blood cells lack nuclei, ERs, ribosomes and mitochondria, and so can only survive for a few months. Found only in animals, their cytoplasm is packed with the protein haemoglobin for transporting oxygen. They are very small and biconcave in shape. This gives them a relatively high surface area for efficient gas exchange.

Cell membranes

Cells are enclosed by a membrane called the **plasma membrane**. In addition, many organelles, such as mitochondria, ER and the nucleus itself are bounded by, or composed of, one or two membranes.

Membranes are exceedingly thin and are made of **phospholipids** and **proteins**. The lipids form two layers of molecules which are mobile. The proteins are found scattered as a mosaic in and on the lipid layers, and they too can move around the membrane. For this reason, the membrane is described as a **fluid-mosaic**.

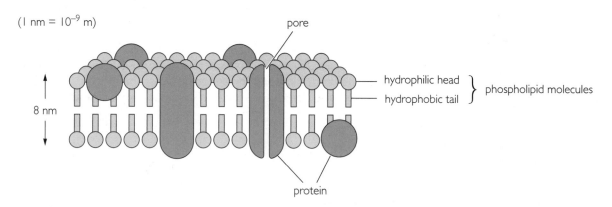

Membranes keep their shape because of the hydrophobic and hydrophilic nature of their lipid molecules. One end of the molecule is repelled by water (hydrophobic) and the other is attracted to water (hydrophilic). As a consequence of their fluidity, membranes can often recover from minor physical damage. Lipids also allow small molecules, such as water molecules, to pass through unaided. The surface area of cells or organelles can be increased by the folding of membranes. (*See diagram of cell and its mitochondria on page 5.*)

Because they are composed of proteins and lipids, membranes are easily damaged by heat, acids and by fat solvents such as alcohol. This can be demonstrated in the laboratory using cells which have a coloured sap such as beetroot or red cabbage. When the membrane of these cells is damaged, the coloured sap leaks out into the surrounding water.

Membrane proteins have many functions. There are:
- enzymes present in membranes for many chemical reactions, e.g. stages in protein synthesis and respiration, which take place on the surface of the membranes
- receptor sites for hormones which then influence the activity of the cell
- proteins which act as a skeleton for the membrane to give it shape and to allow it to move. For example, the membrane moves during phagocytosis and when cilia waft to and fro
- proteins which actively transport materials across the membrane using ATP as a source of energy
- proteins which form pores in the membrane through which substances can pass

Because cells are full of hundreds of different enzymes and millions of molecules which react every second, it is important that the internal environment of the cell is kept as constant as possible. In this respect, the plasma membrane plays a very important function by regulating what enters and leaves the cell. It allows some substances to pass through unaided, while others are transported actively. Some substances are entirely prevented from passing through. For this reason, membranes are said to be **semi** or **selectively permeable**.

Absorption and secretion of materials

Diffusion and osmosis

Atoms and molecules of gases and liquids move about at random. As a result, they tend to spread themselves from areas of high concentration to areas of low concentration. This process is called **diffusion**. **Osmosis** is the term used to describe the diffusion of water across a membrane from a weak solution (high proportion of water molecules) to a strong solution (low proportion of water molecules). A solution which is weaker than another solution is said to be **hypotonic** to the other stronger solution. The stronger solution is **hypertonic** to the weaker solution. Solutions of the same strength are said to be **isotonic**.

Diffusion

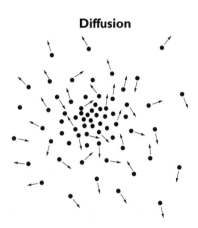

Because all cells are surrounded by a membrane, water can diffuse into and out of cells with ease. Animal cells and plant cells behave differently, however, because animal cells do not have strong supportive porous cell walls surrounding them. The table below shows what can happen to animal and plant cells when placed in solutions of different strengths.

	Hypotonic solution	Hypertonic solution
Animal cells	swell and burst	shrink
Plant cells	become **turgid** (firm)	become **flaccid** (limp)

A plasmolysed cell

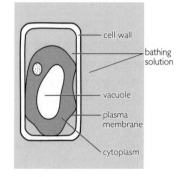

If plant cells are placed in very strong solutions, water is drawn from the cell. In fact, the cytoplasm and vacuole shrink so much that the cell membrane can be pulled away from the cell wall. The cell is then said to be **plasmolysed**.

Plant cell walls are composed principally of **cellulose** fibres which allow free passage of molecules through the gaps between them. Cellulose is composed of many glucose molecules linked together, and as such, is an example of a polysaccharide.

All cells rely on the process of diffusion to absorb and secrete materials. However, diffusion on its own is not sufficient to transport all substances. There are many other ways cells can move substances across membranes. Sometimes substances have to be moved against the way in which they would move naturally by diffusion, i.e. against the **concentration gradient**. This requires energy which is supplied by the cell. The process is called **active transport**, and specialised proteins in cell membranes act as carriers, moving molecules from one side of the membrane to the other using the chemical energy of a compound called **adenosine triphosphate (ATP)**. (ATP is studied later in this unit – see pages 11 to 14.)

Exocytosis

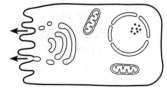

Another way by which substances can move from one side of a membrane to the other is by being enclosed in a tiny membranous sac called a vesicle. The table below summarises the inward and outward movement of materials transported in this way.

Endocytosis	The plasma membrane flows round the substance or particle and encloses it, so bringing it into the cell. (Phagocytosis is an example of endocytosis – see page 18.)
Exocytosis	A vesicle is formed inside the cell from the Golgi body and moves to the plasma membrane where it fuses with it releasing its contents outside the cell. (See diagram above.)

INTO CELL

out of CELL

Photosynthesis

Photosynthesis is the process by which plants with **chlorophyll** manufacture carbohydrate from carbon dioxide and water using light energy from the sun. Oxygen is given off as a by-product.

Plants also contain pigments (coloured substances) other than chlorophyll. These accessory pigments can be extracted from leaves and separated using a simple technique called chromatography. Leaves are crushed up in a solvent such as propanone and the green liquid is then spotted onto chromatography paper. When a concentrated green spot has been produced the paper is dipped in another solvent and left for a few minutes. As the solvent runs up the paper different compounds are carried different distances, according to their molecular shape and size. By dividing the distance a substance has moved by the distance the solvent front has moved up the paper from the origin, the substance's R_f value can be obtained. So R_f values lie between 0 and 1. R_f values can be used in identifying unknown substances. What is the R_f value for chlorophyll *a* in this chromatogram? (*The answer is at the back of this book.*)

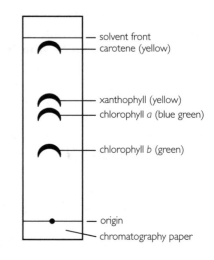

These pigments give leaves their different colours: yellows, shades of green, and even the browns and reds of seaweed fronds and autumnal leaves. However, their purpose is to enable plants to make use of a wider range of wavelengths of light for photosynthesis. This additional light energy is passed on to the chlorophyll *a* molecules which carry out photosynthesis.

Visible light is part of the electromagnetic spectrum. This includes radio waves, X-rays and UV light. By passing 'white' light through a glass prism it is possible to split it into its different component colours, the colours of the rainbow: *red, orange, yellow, green, blue, indigo* and *violet*. Chlorophyll cannot make use of all these colours (wavelengths) of light, so by having other pigments which absorb different colours a wider source of energy is available to the plant. This is particularly useful for plants growing in the 'green' shade of other plants.

The wavelengths of light absorbed by a pigment can be displayed as a graph called the **absorption spectrum**. Because chlorophyll absorbs mostly red and blue light, and reflects green light, it appears green to our eyes.

Is absorbed light actually used by the plant for photosynthesis? This can be checked by growing plants in different colours of light and noting how well they grow. If the results of such an experiment are plotted as a graph, an **action spectrum** is obtained. Rate of photosynthesis can be measured as:

1. volume of carbon dioxide absorbed, or
2. volume of oxygen liberated, or
3. increase in dry mass

all measured over a period of time.

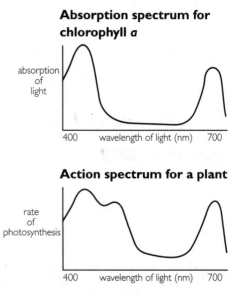

If the two spectral graphs follow a similar pattern then it can be supposed that the light absorbed by a pigment is actually used by the plant for photosynthesis. If the graphs do not follow a similar pattern then it is likely that other pigments are involved in absorbing different wavelengths of light.

Not all the light landing on a leaf is used for photosynthesis. The diagram opposite shows the fates of light landing on a leaf. Normally, less than 5% of the light striking leaves is used for photosynthesis.

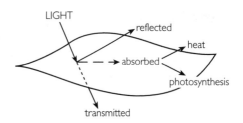

Chloroplasts and photosynthesis

Chloroplasts are possibly the most important structures in the world. They provide the oxygen we breathe, the food we eat, and remove the carbon dioxide we excrete. Moreover, the photosynthetic energy of plants growing millions of years ago now provides us with high-energy fossil fuels. Chloroplasts are full of membranes. If the membranes are in stacks they are called **grana** (singular: granum). The photosynthetic pigments such as **chlorophyll *a*** and ***b*, carotene** and **xanthophyll** are found on these grana and their function is to trap light energy. The energy is passed to the chlorophyll *a* molecules where water is split into hydrogen and oxygen in the '**light reaction**'. The by-product oxygen is released as a result of this **photolysis** of water. The spaces between the membranes are filled with a watery fluid called the **stroma**. The stroma is full of enzymes and other chemicals involved in the second **light independent** stage of photosynthesis, sometimes called the '**dark reaction**' or **Calvin cycle**.

A chloroplast

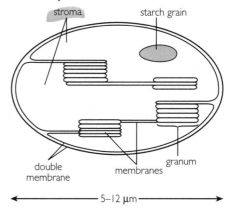

During the Calvin cycle the hydrogen from the water is combined with carbon dioxide in a complex series of reactions to make, among other compounds, **glucose**. The glucose can be:
* broken down during respiration to provide energy-rich ATP for the cell
* stored as starch
* converted to other compounds such as cellulose, the principal component of plant cell walls.

The process of photosynthesis is a two-stage process, one requiring light (the **light dependent** stage, or **light reaction**) and one not requiring light (the **light independent** stage, or **dark reaction** as it used to be called). These two processes are outlined below:

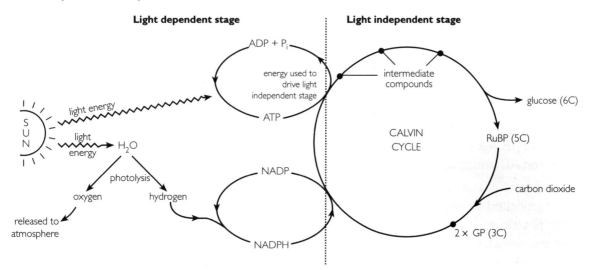

Summary points

In simple terms, carbon dioxide is **reduced** by hydrogen from water to make carbohydrate (CHO).
- The process consists of two stages, the first one (light dependent) requires light energy and the second one (light independent) is powered by the energy of **ATP** which is made during the first stage.
- The first stage occurs in the **grana** of the chloroplast and oxygen is produced as a by-product.
- During the first stage, water molecules are split using light energy. This process is called **photolysis**.
- The hydrogen from the water is carried by a carrier or acceptor compound called **NADP**.
- The second stage:
  - consists of a number of metabolic pathways, each catalysed by different enzymes
  - occurs in the **stroma** of the chloroplast and **glucose** is produced as an end product
  - involves the **fixation** (chemical combination) of carbon.
- During the second stage, carbon dioxide combines with a five-carbon compound called **ribulose bisphosphate** (**RuBP**).
- The six-carbon compound formed turns immediately into two molecules of a three-carbon compound called **glycerate-3-phosphate** (**GP**).
- The GP is then reduced by the addition of hydrogen to form, eventually, **glucose**. At the same time RuBP is regenerated.
- Given a supply of some mineral ions, a plant can make every organic compound (e.g. proteins, fats, nucleic acids and other carbohydrates such as cellulose and starch) it requires using various carbohydrates produced during the Calvin cycle.

Adenosine triphosphate (ATP)

ATP is a compound composed of adenosine and three phosphate groups. ATP is unstable and can lose one or more of its phosphate groups to other molecules. In so doing, chemical energy is transferred to other molecules. Consequently ATP is used in all cells to transfer chemical energy and so drive metabolic processes, e.g. protein synthesis and DNA replication. (*See page 16.*) However, ATP is also used for:
- muscle contraction
- movement of cilia
- movement of sperm tails
- movement of the cell membrane during phagocytosis
- active transport
- movement of chromosomes during mitosis.

When ATP loses one of its phosphate groups (P_i) it becomes adenosine diphosphate (ADP).

The cell needs a constant supply of ATP so it is resynthesised just as quickly as it is broken down. ATP is rather like the chain of a bike, transferring the energy of the cyclist to the back wheels of the bike. The chain never changes mass, nor does the mass of ATP in any cell change. In a typical mammalian cell, around ten million ATP molecules can be consumed and regenerated each second!

ATP is generated during photosynthesis and during a chemical process called **respiration**. ATP generated during photosynthesis is not exported from the chloroplast, but ATP generated during respiration is used to drive the metabolism of the cell. The process of respiration is described on the next two pages.

Respiration

All living things respire, as it is this chemical process which liberates the energy in food to enable functions such as growth, repair and movement to take place. The process is sometimes referred to as 'chemical' or 'tissue' respiration to distinguish it from the common usage of 'respiration' to mean 'breathing'.

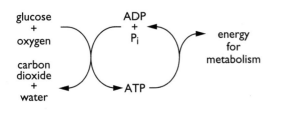

During respiration, various carbon compounds are **oxidised** to produce energy for the synthesis of ATP from ADP and P_i. The ATP can then be used to transfer this chemical energy to drive the metabolic reactions taking place in the cell. The most common compound which is oxidised is glucose.

The process of respiration starts in the cytoplasm of all living cells and continues in the mitochondria if oxygen is present. There are many small steps in this **aerobic** (with oxygen) process to ensure the energy is released in a gradual and controlled way. In essence, hydrogen is removed from glucose ($C_6H_{12}O_6$). This leaves an excess of carbon and oxygen atoms which are released to the atmosphere eventually as carbon dioxide. The hydrogen is then combined with oxygen from the atmosphere to make water. As water is formed, a large quantity of energy becomes available for the synthesis of ATP, so much so that up to **38 molecules** of ATP can be produced from the complete oxidation of only one molecule of glucose.

If no oxygen is available the mitochondria are not involved and cells will respire anaerobically (without oxygen). **Anaerobic respiration** takes place in the cytoplasm only and is much less efficient than **aerobic respiration**. As with aerobic respiration, two molecules of ATP are required to start the process but four molecules are produced as a result. So the **net gain** is two molecules of ATP for every molecule of glucose metabolised. Moreover, during anaerobic respiration toxic compounds, **ethanol** (plants) and **lactic acid** (animals), are produced as end products. Animals can remove lactic acid from their tissues, but plants cannot metabolise ethanol (alcohol), which can build up in the cells and kill the plant.

Plants: glucose → ethanol + carbon dioxide + ATP
Animals: glucose → lactic acid + ATP (Note that no carbon dioxide is produced in animals.)

Brief summary of chemical respiration (aerobic and anaerobic)

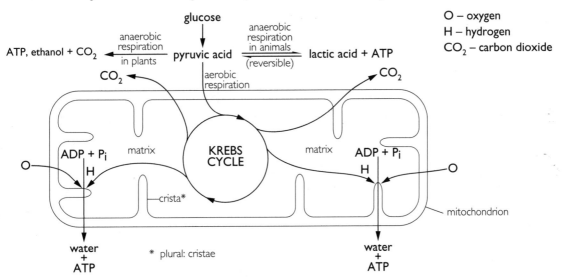

A more detailed outline of chemical respiration

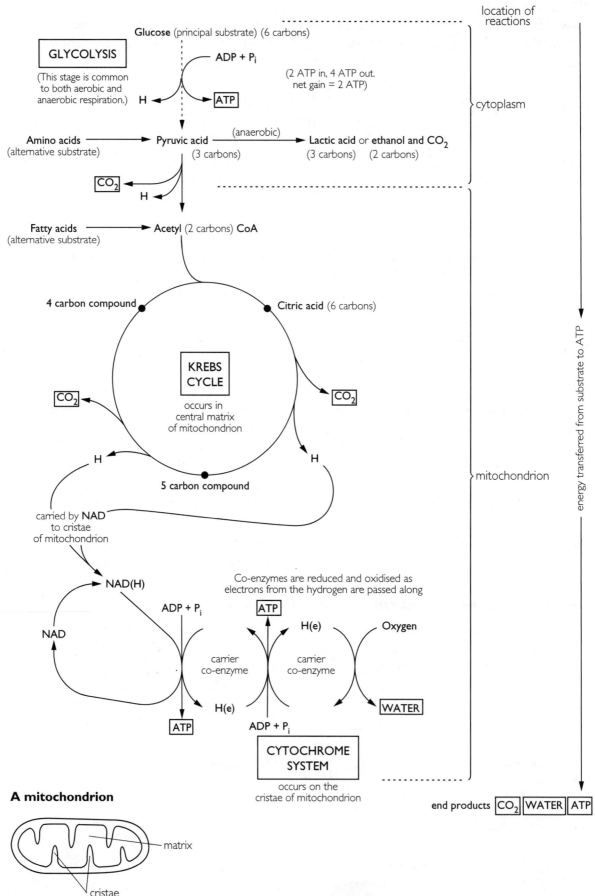

A mitochondrion

The variety and function of proteins

Proteins are **organic*** **compounds** composed of **hydrogen**, **oxygen**, **carbon** and **nitrogen** atoms, sometimes with the addition of various other elements such as sulphur. They are complex molecules with three-dimensional structures which are unique for each protein. There are tens of thousands of different types of protein, and each protein is composed of a large number of building blocks called **amino acids**. Twenty different amino acids are known to occur in nature and numbers of individual amino acids are linked by **peptide bonds** to form chains of various lengths which are folded in complex ways.

Proteins have a multitude of roles to perform in the bodies of animals and plants.
- All enzymes are proteins.
- Many hormones are proteins.
- Muscle is composed mostly of protein.
- Haemoglobin, the oxygen carrier, is a protein.
- Antibodies, which protect our body from infection, are proteins.
- All membranes have a protein component.

Proteins can be classified as **globular** or **fibrous**, and some examples are given in the table below:

Globular proteins	Fibrous proteins
amylase (an enzyme which digests starch)	collagen (a major component of bones, tendons and ligaments)
human growth hormone (see *page 54*)	actin and myosin (muscle fibres)
immunoglobulin (an antibody)	keratin (a major component of hair and skin)

Globular proteins are roughly spherical in shape, whereas fibrous proteins are arranged in long parallel strands which have great tensile strength, i.e. the ability to resist pulling or stretching forces.

A globular protein

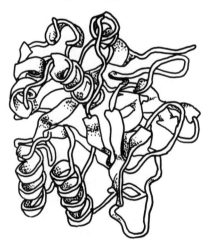

A fibrous protein

The order in which amino acids are put together to form a protein is dictated by the order of **bases** in a molecule called **deoxyribonucleic acid** (**DNA**), which is found in the nucleus of all cells. This process is described on the next two pages.

* Organic compounds contain carbon and often originate from living things.

DNA structure and replication

DNA is the chemical which carries the genetic code ('blueprint') for building an organism, whether it be a bacterium, a plant or an animal. What is more, the code is read in the same way by all organisms. The code is used to link amino acids together in the correct order to make specific proteins. So, DNA dictates which proteins are made by a cell.

DNA is a relatively simple molecule made up of millions of **nucleotides** arranged in two spiralling rows, rather like a twisted ladder. The spiral shape of the molecule was discovered by Watson and Crick in 1952 and is described as a **double helix**. Each nucleotide is composed of a **phosphate** molecule, a **deoxyribose sugar** molecule and a single **base** of which there are four types. The four bases exist in pairs and make up the 'rungs' of the double helix ladder. **Adenine (A)** always pairs with **thymine (T)**, and **guanine (G)** always pairs with **cytosine (C)**. The sequence of these bases dictates the sequence of amino acids in a protein molecule.

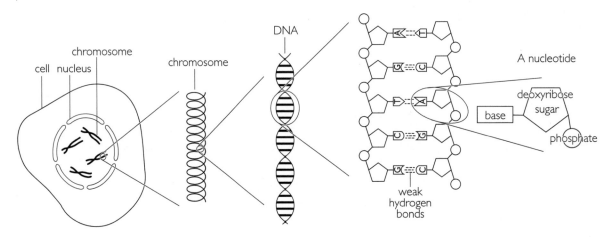

An immensely coiled and folded strand of DNA makes up a **chromosome**. Chromosomes are found in the nucleus of cells and, before any cell divides, a copy of the DNA must be made. This ensures each new cell will have a perfect copy of the instructions, to comply with the design of the organism to which it belongs. This copying process is called **replication** and is catalysed by enzymes.

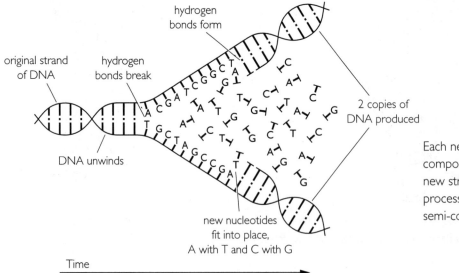

Each new double helix is composed of both an old and a new strand of DNA, so the process is sometimes called semi-conservative replication.

Once the DNA copies have been made, they must be separated and sent to the two new nuclei of the two cells which are to be formed. This process is called **mitosis**. (See *pages 50 and 53.*)

Protein synthesis

Proteins are made at the ribosomes, but the code for protein manufacture resides in the nucleus. So a messenger molecule is needed to carry the code from the nucleus to the ribosomes. This molecule is called **messenger ribonucleic acid (mRNA)**. The transfer of the complimentary code from the DNA to the mRNA is called **transcription**. During transcription, the DNA molecule unwinds and unzips and complementary mRNA bases bind temporarily with the exposed code of part of one of the DNA strands. Start and stop codes tell the mRNA where the code to make a particular protein starts and finishes. Once formed, the mRNA strand leaves the nucleus via a nuclear pore and moves to a ribosome. Ribosomes are found free in the cytoplasm, or attached to the ER. Free ribosomes synthesise proteins for use within the cell; attached ribosomes synthesise proteins for the cell membrane and for export.

RNA is similar to DNA but has a different base (**uracil** instead of thymine) and a different sugar (**ribose**, instead of deoxyribose). Moreover, RNA exists as a **single strand** rather than as a **double strand**. At the ribosomes, a second type of RNA called **transfer RNA (tRNA)** brings in amino acids for assembly into protein. tRNA molecules have three bases (base triplets) called **anti-codons**, which correspond to triplet **codons** of the mRNA.

The code is in threes to allow for the coding of the twenty different **amino acids**. Since the four bases A, C, G and T (or U) can be arranged in threes in sixty-four different ways, many amino acids have more than one code. For example, UUU and UUC both code for the amino acid phenylalanine. In addition, some codes act as 'stop' and 'start' codes.

Example of DNA transcription

DNA code	AAT-CGT-AGG
mRNA codons	UUA-GCA-UCC
tRNA anti-codons	AAU-CGU-AGG

The nine bases in the table will code for three different amino acids, which will make up a small part of a **peptide** chain. A number of peptides linked together make a **polypeptide** and a number of polypeptides linked together make a protein.

The assembly of amino acids, to form proteins, using these triplet codes is described as the **translation** of the RNA code. Once proteins are formed, those which are to be exported from the cell are transported by the **ER** to the **Golgi apparatus** (or **body**) and from there carried in **vesicles** to the cell membrane. (*See page 9.*)

Protein synthesis

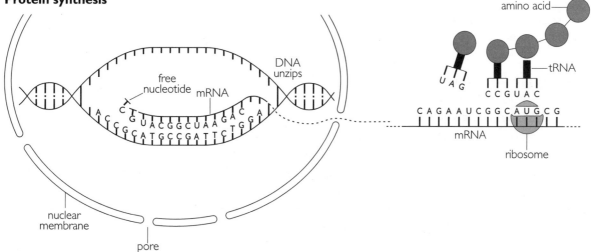

Cell defence and the nature of viruses

We are bombarded by 'germs' of one kind or another throughout our lives. Protists (single cell organisms), fungi, bacteria and viruses are all capable of causing disease. Viruses, in particular, are difficult to deal with. Antibiotics have no effect on them and we have to leave our body's own defence systems to counter-attack. Viruses don't just attack humans, but also cause disease in many organisms: plants, animals and even bacteria.

Viral replication in a bacterium

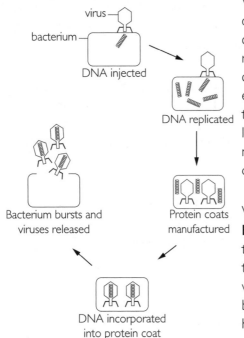

Bacterium bursts and viruses released

DNA injected

DNA replicated

Protein coats manufactured

DNA incorporated into protein coat

Viruses are the smallest known living things. In fact some would question whether they can be classified as living organisms. They cannot reproduce on their own, they do not grow, they do not respire, they do not feed and they do not produce waste. They can be crystallised like simple chemicals and they are invisible except under the most powerful electron microscopes. Despite their size, however, they can have profound effects on other living organisms. This is because they make use of the biochemical machinery of host cells to make copies of themselves and, in so doing, destroy the host cells.

Viruses are made of a **protein coat** containing a **DNA** or **RNA core**. When they combine with host cells they inject their DNA or RNA into the cell. The host cell then comes under the command of the new genetic instructions and makes new viruses using nucleotides, amino acids, ATP and enzymes supplied by the host cell. The new viruses, once formed, burst out of the host cell, killing it in the process. For this reason, organisms suffer symptoms of disease and may even die from a viral infection.

Animals can defend themselves from microbial invasion in a whole variety of ways. First line defences include, for example, tough skins, cilia and mucus in the lungs, acid in the digestive systems and blood which can congeal. If microbes get into the body then two other cellular second line defence systems come in to play. One is non-specific and is found in all vertebrate animals. It involves wandering white blood cells which are able to engulf foreign particles, e.g. bacteria, by **phagocytosis**. Once ingested, the foreign particle is then digested by powerful enzymes contained in special vesicles called **lysosomes**. (See pages 5 and 6.)

Phagocytosis

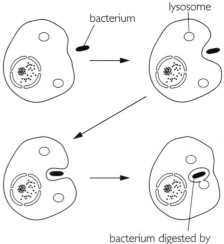

bacterium

lysosome

bacterium digested by enzymes from lysosomes

A second line of defence, found in mammals and birds, is highly specific and involves white blood cells called **lymphocytes**, which belong to the **immune system**. There are a number of different types of lymphocyte, but one type in particular produces chemicals called **antibodies**, which combine with and destroy foreign invaders in a variety of different ways. A microbe such as a bacterium or virus has a distinct protein coat which can be recognised by the immune system as being foreign. Such foreign proteins are called **antigens**. Only specific antibodies can attack specific antigens, so the bodies of vertebrates contain thousands of different lymphocytes, each one designed to produce a specific antibody to combat a specific antigen.

Rejection of tissue transplants

When an organ or tissue is transplanted from one person to another, the immune system of the recipient recognises the transplanted material as foreign. This is because the protein markers on any cells are unique for every individual (except for identical twins). Consequently, the lymphocytes and phagocytes attack the transplanted cells and treat them in the same way as they would any other **pathogen** (disease-causing organism).

There are two ways in which this **tissue rejection** can be minimised. The first is to try to obtain a close match for the protein markers. Surgeons therefore take care to match the antigens of each person as well as they can before carrying out the transplant operation. The second is to suppress the body's immune system using drugs or radiotherapy. The latter treatment is, unfortunately, harmful because it makes the body more open to attack from other pathogens. However, new drugs are now being produced which minimise this effect.

Cellular defence in plants

Plants are subject to attack from pathogens just like animals. Moreover, they are the unwilling food supply of herbivores. So, if anything, they have even more need of protection from physical damage or disease.

Plants do not have immune systems: they have no phagocytic cells and do not produce antibodies. However, they have first line defence systems which include tough cellulose cell walls, and sometimes bark, spines, thorns or stinging cells. They can also protect themselves by producing a variety of compounds which are either toxic or distasteful to herbivores, or by isolating and protecting injured areas by means of substances such as **resin**. Some plants even produce hormones which adversely affect the growth of insects that eat them. Others can produce chemical signals which plants of the same species growing nearby can respond to by producing protective chemicals in advance of an attack.

Many of the protective compounds (e.g. **nicotine**, digitalis, morphine, strychnine, **cyanide** and **tannins**) produced by plants have been used by humans in a variety of ways, for hundreds of years.

Many plant poisons act as enzyme inhibitors, but some are simply distasteful. Resin is distasteful, but also acts as a physical barrier to the penetration of fungal threads. Latex, from which rubber is produced, also acts in this way. Resin and latex are produced in large quantities following physical damage.

Certain species of clover produce hydrogen cyanide in response to damage to their leaves. Hydrogen cyanide acts as a powerful inhibitor of enzymes of the respiratory pathway.

Bracken

Bracken, a fern which is very common in Scotland, produces a variety of toxic compounds, some of which are carcinogenic (cancer causing). Cows and horses, if they eat bracken, very often suffer serious consequences. Because it is so toxic, few herbivores can eat it, so it spreads across cleared woodland and moorland very quickly, and is difficult to eradicate.

Rhododendron is another highly toxic plant of the Scottish countryside, which grazing animals leave well alone. As a consequence, rhododendrons have a competitive advantage over other plants, even spiny ones such as holly and hawthorn. (See *page 49*.)

UNIT TWO — GENETICS, EVOLUTION AND ADAPTATION

This 40-hour unit contains information on variation, meiosis, monohybrid and dihybrid genetics, mutation, natural selection, artificial selection, genetic engineering, maintaining water balance in plants and animals, animal behaviour, and competition and defence mechanisms in animals and plants.

(I) GENETICS
Variation and meiosis

All organisms are different from one another because of the genes they inherit from their parents and because of the effect of the environment. These differences are the basis of evolution. The genetic differences arise mainly from sexual reproduction. During sexual reproduction, **gametes** (sex cells) are produced by a process called **meiosis**. Meiosis is a form of nuclear division, and appears, in many respects, to be like mitosis. (*See pages 50 and 53.*) However, it is profoundly different in that the gametes which result have only half the chromosome number of the parent cells, and that they are all genetically different from one another. These gametes then go on to fuse with others in a random way, so that any new fertilised cell (**zygote**) which is produced has a unique set of genes, different from any other individual. So, for example, you will not find another person the same as yourself (barring identical twins) among the six thousand million humans on this planet. This is because of meiosis!

During meiosis, genes are recombined (shuffled) as a result of two processes:
1. The **crossing over** of pieces of chromosome at points called chiasmata (singular: chiasma).
2. The **independent assortment** of pairs of chromosomes at the equator of the cell.

At fertilisation, the normal chromosome number is regained as a result of the fusion of two gametes, each with a single set of chromosomes. So cells resulting from the fusion of a male and female gamete have two complementary sets of chromosomes which match one another, i.e. the **loci** (positions of the genes) in each set are identical, although the **alleles** (alternatives of the genes) may be different. These matching pairs of chromosomes are called **homologous chromosomes**. (*See karyotype on page 25.*)

At the beginning of meiosis, the homologous chromosomes of **gamete mother cells** find their partners and pair up for a short period of time. Each chromosome already consists of a pair of identical chromatids which have resulted from DNA replication at an earlier stage. When they pair up, the chromatids often break and rejoin at a variety of points called **chiasmata**. As a result, bits of chromatid **cross over** from one chromatid to another. This can be seen in the diagrams on the next page and page 24.

The chromosome pairs then line up along the equator of the cell. They do this independently of one another, so that, when they are pulled to the poles by the spindle fibres, they segregate (separate) independently. This means that two pairs of chromosomes can segregate in two different ways, three pairs in four ways, four pairs in eight ways, and so on. In humans, where there are 23 pairs of chromosomes, this results in 2^{23} (over eight million) different possible combinations. The diagram below shows the different ways in which three pairs of chromosomes can line up along the equator of the cell to give eight different gametes.

The process of meiosis is outlined in detail on the next page. For clarity, only four chromosomes are shown.

Meiosis

Note: chromosomes originating from the male parent are shown shaded; those from the female parent are unshaded.

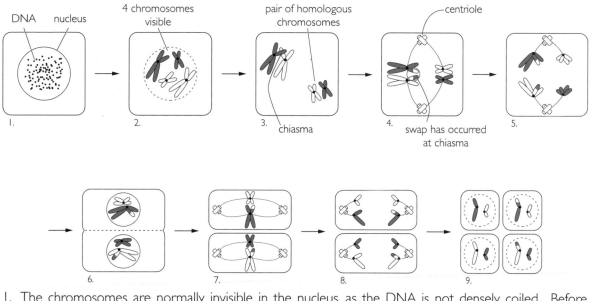

1. The chromosomes are normally invisible in the nucleus, as the DNA is not densely coiled. Before meiosis can take place, the DNA must replicate so that there are two copies of the genes to share out to the new cells which are about to be formed.

2. The nuclear membrane disappears. The chromosomes start to shorten and thicken and eventually become visible as tiny dark threads. They can be seen as pairs of **chromatids** joined at a point called the centromere. These chromatids are identical copies of DNA formed during the earlier replication process.

3. The chromosomes find their homologous partners and the chromatids become intertwined at chiasmata. At these points the chromatids often break and rejoin with their opposite number and genes cross over from one chromatid to another. This does not happen in mitosis.

4. The homologous pairs of chromosomes migrate to the equator of the cell and line up in pairs independently of one another. Spindle fibres form from the centrioles and become attached to the chromosomes at their centromeres.

5. The homologous chromosomes are pulled apart towards opposite ends of the cell by the spindle fibres.

6. Once the chromosomes have reached the poles of the cell, the cell divides in two. Now each new cell has only two chromosomes and not four. The cells are **haploid**, not **diploid**.

7. The two cells go on to divide to form four gametes (e.g. sperm, eggs, pollen). This second meiotic division is very similar to a mitotic division. Chromosomes align on the equator of the cell individually, and not in homologous pairs as before.

8. The spindle fibres form and become attached to the chromatids which they pull apart.

9. Four cells are formed, each with two chromatids which can now be called chromosomes again. Some chromatids will be different from others because of the crossing over of genes at chiasmata. Moreover, the combination of chromatids in each cell will be different because of the random way in which they lined up along the equator of the cell at the first and second division of meiosis.

Monohybrid inheritance

Sexually reproducing organisms possess two **genes** for every characteristic, one inherited from each parent. These alternative genes are called **alleles**. If just one of these alleles affects the development of an individual it is said to be **dominant** over the other **recessive** allele. Recessive alleles have no effect on the **phenotype** (appearance) of the individual unless paired with another recessive allele. For simplicity, alleles are represented by letters of the alphabet. A dominant allele is written with a capital letter and a recessive allele is written with a small letter. Organisms with two identical alleles for any particular characteristic (trait) are said to be **homozygous**, whereas those with two different alleles are **heterozygous**. The genetic make-up of an individual is referred to as the **genotype**. In any cross the parents are referred to as the **P** generation, and thereafter their **progeny** (offspring) are called the F_1 and F_2 generations, etc.

A hundred and sixty years ago an Austrian Monk called Gregor Mendel worked out some simple rules on the inheritance of genes, although he called them 'particles'. He worked with pea plants in the monastery for many years, crossing one type with another and counting the numbers of different offspring from each cross. Sadly, his work went unnoticed, and it was not until the beginning of the last century, when other scientists rediscovered the principles of inheritance, that Mendel's work was given due credit.

Mendel usually started with **true breeding** pea plants. This means that the pea plants always produced offspring with the same characteristics as themselves. For example, true breeding Labradors would be expected to have only Labrador pups.

One of Mendel's crosses involved crossing true breeding *tall* plants with true breeding *dwarf* plants. When he examined the offspring, he found them all to be tall. However, when he allowed these tall plants to interbreed, dwarf ones appeared again in the second generation in the ratio of about 3 tall to 1 dwarf. How this happened is explained below.

The plants each have two alleles for height; this is because they received one allele for height from each of their parents. An outline of the crosses is given below:

Parents (P)

Phenotype (appearance)	**Tall** × **Dwarf**
Genotype (letters representing alleles)	**TT** × **tt** (both homozygous)
Gametes (sex cells with half the number of alleles)	**T** × **t**
F_1 Genotype	All **Tt** (heterozygous)
F_1 Phenotype	All **Tall**

This result confirms that the phenotype *tall* is dominant to *dwarf*.

When the F_1 generation is allowed to interbreed the following would be expected to occur:

F_1 Phenotype	**Tall** × **Tall**
F_1 Genotype	**Tt** × **Tt** (both heterozygous)
Gametes	**T** or **t** × **T** or **t**

Each gamete **T** and **t** is produced in equal numbers because of the separation of chromosomes at meiosis, but because each parent produces two different types of gametes, there are four ways in which these might combine at random. This is shown in the diagram below, which is called a Punnett square.

Punnett square

Gametes	T	t
T	TT	Tt
t	Tt	tt

The shaded boxes show the possible genotypes of the F_2 generation.

From the diagram there would be an expectation that three quarters (75%) of the offspring would grow tall and, of these, one third would be homozygous. This explains Mendel's 3:1 ratio of the F_2 generation. However, an exact 3:1 ratio is rarely achieved because the process of fertilisation is random, i.e. the fusion of gametes is open to chance, just like the toss of a coin. If tossed 100 times, you would expect 50 heads and 50 tails but if you got 48 heads and 52 tails you would not be surprised.

Dihybrid inheritance

If two characteristics are considered at the same time, the situation becomes more complex. Imagine a cross between pea plants which have *round* and *yellow* seeds (both dominant) and pea plants which have *wrinkled* and *green* seeds. The plants are pure bred, i.e. homozygous, so all the offspring have the same genotype.

Parents	**RRYY**	×	**rryy**
Gametes	**RY**	×	**ry**
F_1 generation	**RrYy**		

Because *all* the offspring have seeds which are *round* and *yellow*, this confirms two facts:
1. the parents are true breeding (homozygous)
2. *round* and *yellow* are both dominant characteristics.

What now happens if the F_1 generation is crossed with itself? i.e. **RrYy × RrYy**

As a consequence of meiosis, an individual with the genotype **RrYy** can produce four different types of gamete, so long as the genes for shape and colour are not **linked**, i.e. so long as they are on separate chromosomes. These gametes are **RY**, **Ry**, **rY** and **ry**. Therefore the Punnett square is not 2 x 2, but 4 x 4.

Gametes	RY	Ry	rY	ry
RY	RRYY	RRYy	RrYY	RrYy
Ry	RRYy	RRyy	RrYy	Rryy
rY	RrYY	RrYy	rrYY	rrYy
ry	RrYy	Rryy	rrYy	rryy

F_2 generation

Check the phenotypes of the F_2 generation and record the numbers of each phenotype. (*The answer is at the back of the book.*)

From the table on the previous page, it can be seen that if a plant has seeds which are *round* and *yellow* its genotype could be any one of four different types. In a real-life situation the genotype of such a plant can be discovered using a 'back' or 'test cross'. This is a cross with a plant which is homozygous recessive for both characteristics (**rryy**).

The table below shows the results of these four crosses.

Parent: round yellow	Parent: wrinkled green	Genotypes of offspring	Phenotypes of offspring
RRYY	rryy	RrYy	All round and yellow
RRYy	rryy	RrYy and Rryy	All round, but only half yellow
RrYY	rryy	RrYy and rrYy	All yellow, but only half round
RrYy	rryy	RrYy, Rryy, rrYy and rryy	Four phenotypes in equal numbers

Because the results in all four crosses are different, it is then possible to determine the unknown genotypes of the four round-yellow seeded plants.

Linkage

Sometimes, however, the results turn out to be unexpected, e.g. a cross of **RrYy** with **rryy** might produce offspring in numbers which are not remotely close to the expected ratio of 1:1:1:1. In such a case, we must conclude that the genes are linked, i.e. on the same chromosome. The effect of gene linkage is explained as follows: imagine that gene **R** is linked to **Y**, and **r** to **y**. From **Figure 1** it can be seen that only two types of gamete are formed, not four. This is because at meiosis, when gametes are formed, **R** always travels on the same chromosome as **Y**, and **r** with **y** to give equal numbers of **RY** and **ry** gametes

Figure 1 – production of gametes from parent RrYy (no crossover)

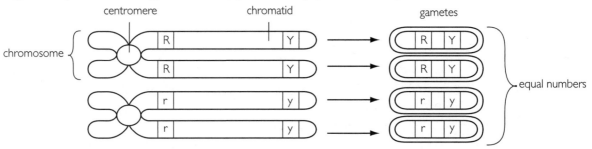

However, sometimes crossovers occur and two new gametes arise as shown in **Figure 2**. These new **recombinant** gametes are rare because crossovers are not particularly frequent. In fact, the percentage recombination of **R** with **y** and **r** with **Y** to give F₁ offspring **Rryy** and **rrYy** gives a good indication of the distance genes are apart on a chromosome. The further they are apart, the more likely a crossover will separate them and the more often **Rryy** and **rrYy** will turn up. Information from a series of test crosses can then be used to map the position of genes on a chromosome. (*See next page.*)

Figure 2 – production of gametes from parent RrYy (with crossover)

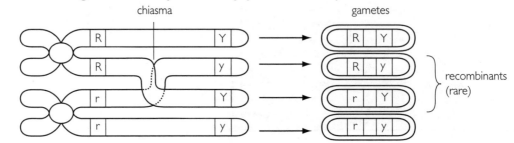

Gene mapping

Imagine four linked genes **A**, **B**, **C** and **D**.
The table below shows the results of four test crosses.

Parents	Offspring – percentage recombination*
AaBb × aabb	5% of the offspring are **Aabb** or **aaBb**
AaCc × aacc	2% of the offspring are **Aacc** or **aaCc**
CcDd × ccdd	3% of the offspring are **Ccdd** or **ccDd**
BbDd × bbdd	4% of the offspring are **Bbdd** or **bbDd**

* The percentage recombination is sometimes known as the crossover value.

Try to map the relative positions of these genes on the chromosome.
For example, A is further from B than from C, and D is closer to C than B.
(*The answer is at the back of the book.*)

Sex linkage

The sex of humans, and many other organisms for that matter, is controlled by a pair of **sex chromosomes**. In most organisms, the female has a pair of identical X-chromosomes, and the male has a pair of non-identical chromosomes, called the X- and Y-chromosomes. The Y-chromosome is shorter than the X-chromosome and it is the Y-chromosome which confers masculinity. The sex chromosomes are therefore an exception to the rule that homologous chromosomes are identical in appearance. This can be seen in the karyotype of a human male shown opposite.

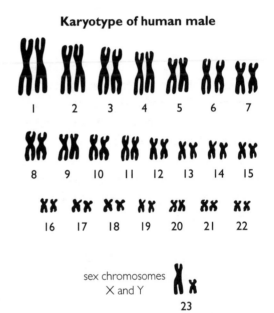

Karyotype of human male

sex chromosomes
X and Y
23

In humans all eggs must have an X-chromosome as a result of meiosis. In males, the sperm can be either X- or Y-sperm. If an X-sperm fertilises an egg then a girl results, and if a Y-sperm fertilises an egg then a boy results. Because of the way in which the X- and Y-chromosomes separate at meiosis, 50% of sperm must be X-sperm, and 50% must be Y-sperm. It is for this simple reason that most populations of sexually reproducing organisms contain equal numbers of males and females.

However, the rules of inheritance break down with genes found on the sex chromosomes. This is because the X-chromosome has many genes not found on the Y-chromosome. So it does not matter whether a gene on the unpaired portion of an X-chromosome is dominant or recessive; it will always affect the phenotype of the male organism, because there is no dominant allele on the Y-chromosome to mask it.

unpaired
genes

X Y

For example, in humans, red-green colour blindness and haemophilia are sex-linked recessive conditions. Haemophilia is a condition in which the blood fails to clot properly. It used to be a fatal condition, but can be treated now. If a man with normal blood marries a woman with normal blood, but who carries the recessive allele for haemophilia, then the chances of them having a child with haemophilia can be calculated using a Punnett square. This is shown on the next page.

The female parent is XX and one of the X-chromosomes carries the dangerous recessive allele (h). The male parent is XY and his Y chromosome has no locus (position) on it for a blood-clotting gene.

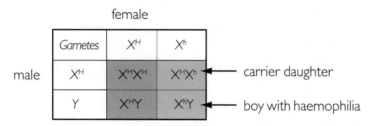

It can be seen from the Punnett square that all the daughters will be healthy, whereas there is a 50% chance that a boy might inherit the haemophilic condition. There is also a 50% chance that any daughter they have might be a carrier. Boys cannot be carriers of the allele, because they cannot be heterozygous.

Note: Not all organisms inherit sex in this manner. In some (e.g. birds) the females are XY and in others, (e.g. some insects) the males have an X-chromosome, but no Y-chromosome.

Mutation

Meiosis, followed by random fertilisation, results in an almost infinite variety of gene combinations in any species of plant or animal which reproduces sexually. However, meiosis can only recombine genes which already exist — it cannot create new genes. New genes arise as a result of **mutations**. These new genes are the essential ingredients of evolution, because sometimes they give an organism a feature which improves its chances of survival in a changing world. For example, in humans, the mutation giving rise to sickle-cell anaemia gives some protection to heterozygotes from the disease malaria. However, the vast majority of mutations are harmful because they change a gene programme of an organism that has been perfected over millions of years of evolution. For example, if the wrong enzyme is made a metabolic pathway will be blocked. (*See page 54.*)

Mutations are random, undirected, spontaneous changes in DNA molecules. They can be as simple as a change in one base, or as significant as a change in large parts, or even numbers, of entire chromosomes in a cell. Mutations can, and do, occur in any nucleated cells, but those occurring in gametes are of particular significance because they are inherited.

Anything which causes a mutation is called a **mutagen**. Shorter wavelengths of radiation are particularly dangerous. Alpha (α), beta (β) gamma (γ) and X-rays, which are emitted from nuclear reactions and atomic explosions, increase mutation rate, and can be lethal if they reach sufficient intensity. So the mutation rate of all life on Earth has increased in the last sixty years due to the testing of atomic bombs and the operation of nuclear power stations. Fortunately, mutation rates are still very low, and mutations are usually recessive. The average mutation rate is 10^{-5} per locus per generation, i.e. 1 in 100 000.

Pregnant women are rarely X-rayed, to avoid causing mutations in the developing embryonic tissues of the foetus. Moreover, people working with X-ray machines have to be protected in one way or other from this dangerous radiation. UV light and many toxic chemicals are also mutagenic. Cigarette smoke causes cancer of the lungs, and sunbathing increases the risk of skin cancer. Cancer results from mutations arising in somatic (body) cells, where these mutated cells divide and multiply in an uncontrolled way. If malignant, these cells spread throughout the body and cause new cancerous growth in other tissues.

There are many different ways in which mutations can occur. In gene mutations, individual bases can be added, substituted or deleted from a strand of DNA. **Substitutions** often have little effect because they change only one triplet code and might affect only one amino acid in a protein chain. However, **deletions** and **insertions** are much more serious, because they alter the subsequent code for every amino acid in the chain. Such changes are called 'frame shift' mutations.

Mutations

AUG/CCC/GGC/AAU	normal mRNA
AUG/*CUC*/GGC/AAU	substitution (U for C)
AUG/*CCG/GCA/AU*...	deletion (take out C)
AUG/*CCA/CGG/CAA/U*	insertion (add A)
(affected codes in italics)	

Chromosome mutations can result in pieces of chromosome being removed (**deletion**), rotated and replaced (**inversion**), shifted from one place to another (**translocation**), or copied twice (**duplication**).

Non-disjunction

Occasionally, entire extra chromosomes arise in gametes, through a failure of the spindle fibres to pull one or more of the chromosomes apart at meiosis. This meiotic failure is called **non-disjunction**. Most of these non-disjunction mutations are lethal, but a few are not. For example, in humans, an extra chromosome, number 21, causes **Down's syndrome**. This arises when an abnormal gamete with 24 chromosomes fuses with a normal one containing 23 chromosomes.

Non-disjunction

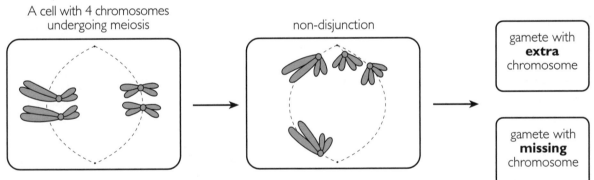

A cell with 4 chromosomes undergoing meiosis — non-disjunction — gamete with **extra** chromosome — gamete with **missing** chromosome

Complete non-disjunction

Sometimes, all the chromosomes in a cell move in the same direction at meiosis and some diploid gametes result. If a diploid gamete fuses with a haploid gamete then the zygote (fertilised egg) will have three sets of chromosomes (triploid). If two diploid gametes fuse then a zygote will form with four sets of chromosomes (tetraploid). If such zygotes are viable (able to live) then the new organism which develops will have more than two sets of chromosomes and be called a **polyploid**. Polyploidy is very common in plants, but not in animals.

Polyploidy

In the production of crop plants, species with entire extra sets of chromosomes often grow much stronger and have a greater yield. So plant breeders often induce polyploidy artificially using irradiation or chemicals such as colchicine. Colchicine interferes with the mitotic division of the zygote by stopping the spindle fibres from developing. Then the two sets of chromatids are not separated and the zygote becomes tetraploid.

The table below summarises the terms used to describe the chromosome numbers of cells.

Chromosome number	Type of cell	Term
n	gamete (sex cell)	**haploid**
2n	normal body cell (somatic cell)	**diploid**
3n, 4n or more	cell with one or more extra sets of chromosomes	**polyploid**

For example, plants in the group known as the *Brassicas* are thought to have originated from three species – cabbage, black mustard and turnip. Some *Brassica* species are shown in the table below.

Name of plant species	Diploid no.
swede	38
brown mustard	36
Abyssinian mustard	34
turnip	20
cabbage	18
black mustard	16

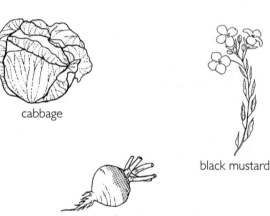

cabbage

turnip

black mustard

For example, it is likely the swede originated from a cross between a turnip and a cabbage. The turnip produces haploid gametes with a chromosome number of 10 and the cabbage produces haploid gametes with a chromosome number of 9. Because they are closely related, the gametes can fuse to give a new plant with a diploid number of 19. However, this new **hybrid** plant is sterile, because its cells cannot undergo meiosis. This confirms that cabbage and turnip are different species, because, although they can interbreed, their offspring are sterile. The reason the gamete mother cells cannot undergo meiosis is simple. The two sets of chromosomes from the parents don't quite match, i.e. they are not perfectly homologous. Moreover, in this example, there is an uneven number, so there will be one chromosome with no partner at all.

However, if the zygote's chromatids fail to separate during mitosis, then the chromosome number will be doubled to 38. What is more, every chromosome will then have an identical homologous partner. So the new polyploid plant will be fertile; its diploid number will be 38 and it will be a swede!

Try to link two other parent plants with their polyploid derivative. (*The answer is at the back of the book.*)

(II) EVOLUTION
Natural selection and speciation

One might argue that humans first became conscious beings when they asked the questions: 'Who are we?' 'Where do we come from?' 'Why do we exist?' Many have sought to provide an answer to this fundamental mystery, and one of the commonest solutions is to believe that a supernatural Deity has arranged it so. However, in the middle of the nineteenth century an English naturalist, Charles Darwin, proposed a mechanism which did not rely on any supernatural force for its explanation. He proposed that living things were not immutable (unchanging) as many believed at the time. He suggested that they had arisen from primitive common ancestors millions of years before and, through a series of gradual changes, had evolved to present day forms. He was not the first to suggest that species could change, but he provided a simple mechanism by which the process could be explained.

Darwin noticed that organisms had the potential to produce large numbers of offspring. However, it was also quite clear that most populations remained fairly stable over a long period of time. So it was evident that some organisms died before they could reproduce. Darwin also noticed that the offspring of any sexually reproducing organism all differed. He concluded, therefore, that those with advantageous characteristics were more likely to survive and pass on these characteristics to their offspring. Over a long period of time these changes might accumulate to cause new species to arise. His theory is widely accepted by the biological world today and is known as the theory of **natural selection**. However, Darwin knew nothing of chromosomes, genes or Mendel's laws of inheritance, although Mendel had published his work at around the same time as Darwin published his book *The Origin of Species*.

Expressed in modern biological terms we can say that organisms produced by sexual reproduction are all slightly different because of gene shuffling at meiosis. In addition, new genes arise by chance mutations. Genes which give an organism an advantage over its neighbours in an ecosystem are more likely to be passed on to the next generation, because the organism they have built is more likely to survive to reproduce. Genes that are disadvantageous are more likely to be lost, because that organism may die before it can reproduce. Accumulated changes in genes in an isolated population over a long period of time will then lead to the evolution of a new species.

For example, a gene which makes a cheetah a little faster than its neighbour will give it a slight advantage when it comes to chasing prey. The cheetah will be more likely to survive because it can catch food more easily and so that gene is more likely to be passed on to its offspring. Life is not so simple of course, because the same principles apply to its prey!  Moreover, high speed is not the only way to catch prey. Co-operation with others of the same species (lions), and endless patience and the ability to climb trees (leopards) are also advantageous features. The problems of surviving on Earth can be solved in a myriad of ways.

The concept is very simple. So simple in fact that Thomas Huxley, a friend and supporter of Darwin, commented: 'How very foolish of me not to have thought of that!'

Darwin's theory of evolution by natural selection describes a mechanism whereby changes in the genotypes, and hence phenotypes, of organisms can take place over a number of generations. New features which better equip an organism to survive are favoured, while less useful features are weeded out as their owners die before they can reproduce. So over a long period of time one species may change so much that it could be called a new species. At what point though, in this gradual process, does the new form become sufficiently different from the original form to be called a new species? It is not easy to fix a point, but a common definition which works reasonably well in most situations is to say that when the two groups of organisms can no longer breed to produce fertile offspring, then they belong to two distinct species. In the example given above, this test can never be carried out because the new form has evolved over hundreds or thousands of years from an older form which no longer exists. In a sense the original form has become **extinct**, yet it hasn't because its progeny live on!

Some species, of course, cannot adapt quickly enough to changing conditions, e.g. new predators, changing climate, disease or human interference. They too become extinct, but in a permanent way, because their progeny no longer exist, even in a different form.

For two or more species to be generated from an original single species the extra dimension required is **isolation**. There are many forms of isolation. Animals can become separated by behavioural differences, e.g. when they migrate or mate. Or they could become sexually isolated by changes in the way they reproduce. However, the easiest form of isolation to understand is that of **geographical isolation**.

Darwin, in his voyage round the world, visited the Galapagos islands, some 600 miles off the west coast of South America. These islands provide an excellent example of the effect of geographical isolation on evolution. The islands arose from the ocean bed as volcanic islands, some seven million years ago. Therefore all animals or plants living there must have come from somewhere else, most likely the mainland of South America. What struck Darwin was that the Galapagos species were not the same as the mainland species. For example, the tortoises, iguanas (see page 61) and finches were all different. What is more, there were *different* species of these animals on *different* islands. So he concluded that they must have changed *after* their arrival on the islands. They must have evolved.

The conditions on the islands were different from the mainland (e.g. different predators, vegetation and weather) so the island species evolved over many years to a point where they became technically unable to breed with the mainland species. (They never had the opportunity in any case, as they were too far away!) At that point in time new species could be said to have arisen.

Why then did so many different species of finch evolve on the islands themselves? It is likely that the first flock of birds to be blown to the islands in some storm were probably the first land birds to arrive. Therefore there were no other land birds there to compete with for ecological niches. The finches could become seed eaters, insect eaters or fruit eaters – they had the place to themselves! It must be remembered, however, that isolation of one form or another is still needed to explain the appearance of these different species of finch. It is likely that they were able to evolve separately because there are many islands in the Galapagos archipelago and each group of finches was sufficiently isolated from the others to prevent cross breeding. This type of evolution, where related groups of organisms from ancestral populations have adapted to new environments and diverged to form a number of distinct species, is called **adaptive radiation**.

Darwin's finches showing different beaks for different purposes

High speed evolution

Organisms have to live to a reproductive age, produce offspring and die, before evolution can take place. So it follows, if an organism can do this quickly and produce lots of offspring, then it can evolve more quickly. If you can 'breed like a rabbit' you can survive like a rabbit! That is not to say that rabbit populations increase, simply that they have the *potential* to increase very quickly and therefore to *adapt* very quickly.

In recent times, environments have been changing very rapidly due to human influences. If an organism can adapt to a changing environment then it can survive; if it cannot it will become extinct. Sadly, many species are becoming extinct every year as a result of human 'progress'. However, some fast breeders can cope with our interference. Rabbits, rats, insects, bacteria and many plants offer examples of this 'high speed' adaptation to a changing environment because of their ability to produce large numbers of progeny quickly.

Rabbits

Rabbits were able to adapt to the viral disease myxomatosis which humans introduced to Britain around fifty years ago to try to wipe them out. Then, mutations in their genes made some of them more resistant to the disease and the mutant rabbits were better able to deal with the virus. They survived to reproduce, so now Britain is populated by rabbits which are fairly resistant to myxomatosis. Incidentally, viruses evolve too, and very often they evolve to become less virulent. A virus which kills its host quickly reduces its chances of moving on to another body!

Rats

Rats have become resistant to the poison warfarin because a mutation occurred many years ago which gave resistance to this poison. Rats which do not have the gene are removed from the population if warfarin is used by farmers, whereas rats which do have the gene have a selective advantage and survive. This new gene is then passed on to their offspring.

Bacteria

One bacterium can divide to form two in an hour quite easily. If one bacterium divides in two, then these two divide again to produce four, then eight, then sixteen bacteria, and so on; after 24 hours, given ideal conditions, there would be 2^{24} (over 16 million) bacteria. So it is not surprising that mutants which are resistant to antibiotics have turned up. Consequently, medical research has to continually develop new antibiotics to stay one step ahead of the evolution of bacteria. Don't be surprised if your doctor is sometimes reluctant to prescribe antibiotics, because (1) the more often they are used the more likely it is that bacteria will become resistant to them and (2) antibiotics do not affect viruses.

Grass

Many plants have become resistant to poisonous substances. For example, some grasses have adapted to live on the toxic waste tips left from the mining of metals such as copper and lead. By acquiring resistance, they can make use of a habitat where the poisons keep out other competitors.

The peppered moth
light form

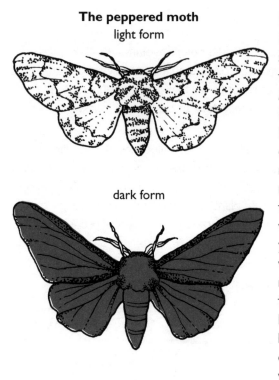

dark form

Insects

Many insects are now resistant to insecticides such as DDT, and many house plant pests, such as greenfly, are resistant to house plant insecticides. The peppered moth (*Biston betularia*) is a well-known example of adaptation by an insect to a change in the environment brought about by human activity. The moth is normally a speckled grey in colour. Occasionally a mutation occurs which makes the moth black. Normally, in the countryside, these 'melanic' moths are easily spotted by birds and eaten. As a result, there are never many black moths to be seen. However, with the arrival of the Industrial Revolution two hundred years ago, the environment near the cities was blackened with the soot from millions of chimneys. As a result, the mutant black moths became invisible to the predators and the speckled grey ones were spotted and eaten. Before long, the woodlands near the cities became populated by black moths, rather than grey ones. This is an example of one small step in the evolutionary process which has been witnessed within a short period of time.

Conservation of species

In comparison with those examples given above, animals such as tigers, pandas, blue whales and gorillas reproduce rather slowly and have few offspring. So they are at serious risk of extinction as a result of hunting, poaching and habitat destruction. It is a well-known fact that the activities of humans over the past three or four hundred years have resulted in the mass extinction of many species. Many people are concerned, and much has been done to try to conserve species.

Panda

Rhinoceros

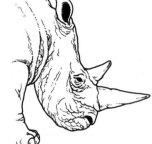

In many countries there are laws, for example, to:
- prohibit the collection of eggs
- ensure sustainable logging of timber
- limit the hunting of animals
- limit the trading in animal products, e.g. rhino horn, elephant tusk, animal skins and furs.

In addition, there are:
- captive breeding programmes in zoos
- cell banks to store gametes and seeds
- nature reserves where animals and plants are protected
- wildlife parks for tourists to generate much needed cash
- financial incentives to reduce the clearing of tropical forest.

Tiger

A key feature in these programmes is to maintain genetic diversity. When only a few members of one species are left to breed, then inbreeding takes place. In these circumstances, harmful recessive genes are more likely to pair up and affect the phenotype.

Artificial selection

We have all said at one time or another that butterflies have wings so that they can fly, and bright colours to startle their predators; their proboscis is like a coiled straw so that it can suck nectar from flowers. These statements imply design by a Creator, but Darwin's theory enables us to remove the need for purposeful design. Mutations, and their consequent effect on phenotype, occur by chance and are passed on to the next generation only if they result in an organism surviving to breed. Natural selection has no plan for the future, no foresight, no consciousness – it just happens. This is not to say that it is a purely random process like the run of a roulette wheel. If it were, the process of evolution would not have gone very far along the road to producing anything so complex as a butterfly. The occurrence of mutations is random and undirected, but the *selection* of useful mutations is not random, and it is for this reason such wonderful creatures as butterflies have evolved on earth.

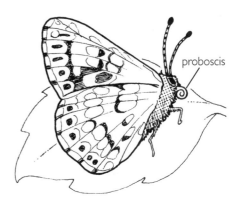

However, as is often the case, there is an exception to the rule. Not all creatures on Earth have arisen without the intervention of a purposeful creator. The creator and designer 'Man' has tinkered with the processes of evolution to produce crop plants and domesticated animals by artificially selecting animals and plants with a purpose in mind. The weaker offspring are killed and the useful ones are kept for further breeding. The greyhound has been bred for speed, the Jersey cow for creamy milk, the Golden Wonder potato for making crisps! What is more, artificial selection is far quicker than natural selection. One only has to compare domesticated dogs with their wild cousins to see how effective a few thousand years of artificial selection has been. Up to very recent times, however, we have had to let nature produce the mutants and we have simply selected the ones most suited to our purposes. Now, however, with the tools of genetic engineering, we can induce mutations and transfer genes from one species to another. The pace of evolution has never been so fast.

Ancestry of domesticated dogs

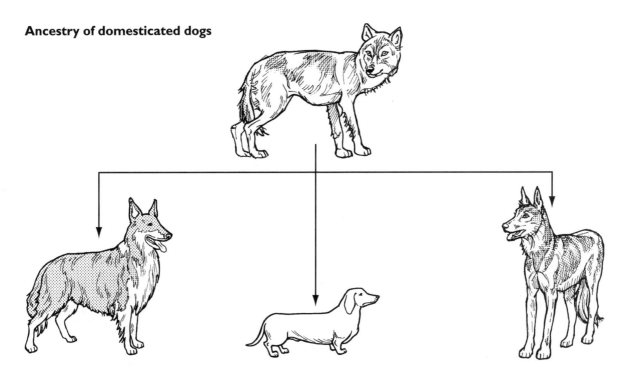

Genetic engineering

Genetic engineering is the transfer of genes from one species of organism to another enabling the second organism to produce a specific protein, e.g. an enzyme or hormone.

Genes are composed of strands of DNA, and the A,C,G,T gene code is read in the same way by every living organism on Earth – powerful evidence that all life on Earth has evolved from common ancestry. For this reason, it is now possible to transfer genes from one organism to another. For example, the code to make the hormone **insulin** can be transferred from a human cell to the **plasmid** of a bacterium such as **Escherichia coli**. This results in the bacterium producing 'human' insulin. Insulin is needed to treat diabetes, and because the **recombinant** bacteria can be **cloned** to produce vast numbers of bacteria it is very easy to produce human insulin on an industrial scale. Plasmids are rings of DNA in bacteria which can be used by the bacteria to transfer genetic information, such as antibiotic resistance, to one another. For this reason plasmids are relatively easy to remove from, and replace into, bacterial cells.

The process of transferring genes from one cell to another requires enzymes to open cells, and probes to identify the required genes. Then the following enzymes are used:
1. **reverse transcriptase** to transcribe RNA back to DNA
2. **endonuclease** to cut DNA strands in specific places
3. **ligase** to glue in the new required gene codes.

The diagram opposite outlines the process in the manufacture of human insulin. mRNA is targeted rather than DNA because, in the pancreas where the cells are actively manufacturing insulin, there is a great deal of RNA with the appropriate insulin code. **Human growth hormone** (HGH) can be made in the same way. (*See page 54.*)

Gene probes

The locating of genes in the genome of an organism could be described as like searching for a needle in a haystack. One of the techniques used to find genes is to use **gene probes**. These consist of strands of DNA or RNA which have been made **radioactive** and which have a sequence of bases on them which is complementary to the required gene. This sequence can be worked out by knowing a short amino acid sequence present in the required protein. The RNA can then be synthesised artificially using radioactive molecules. This RNA is added to a sample of DNA fragments, some of which contain the required gene. The DNA containing this gene becomes radioactive because the RNA attaches itself (by base pairing with hydrogen bonds) to the target strands of DNA. The DNA which is radioactive can be identified by exposing all the DNA to a photographic plate, or photographic film. The radioactive DNA makes black marks on the film. Such marked film is called an **autoradiograph**. This technique can also be used to find bacteria which have picked up a required gene. By comparing the position of the black marks with the position of the colonies of bacteria on an agar plate, it is then possible to identify the bacteria which contain the desired gene.

Banding patterns

When chromosomes are stained with certain dyes, they show characteristic banding patterns which are unique for each chromosome. This feature can be used to pair homologous chromosomes when establishing a karyotype. (*See page 25.*) If a mutated chromosome is examined, the banding pattern is often different. So differences in the banding pattern indicate where the mutation occurred and therefore where the mutant gene is located.

The manufacture of insulin by genetic engineering

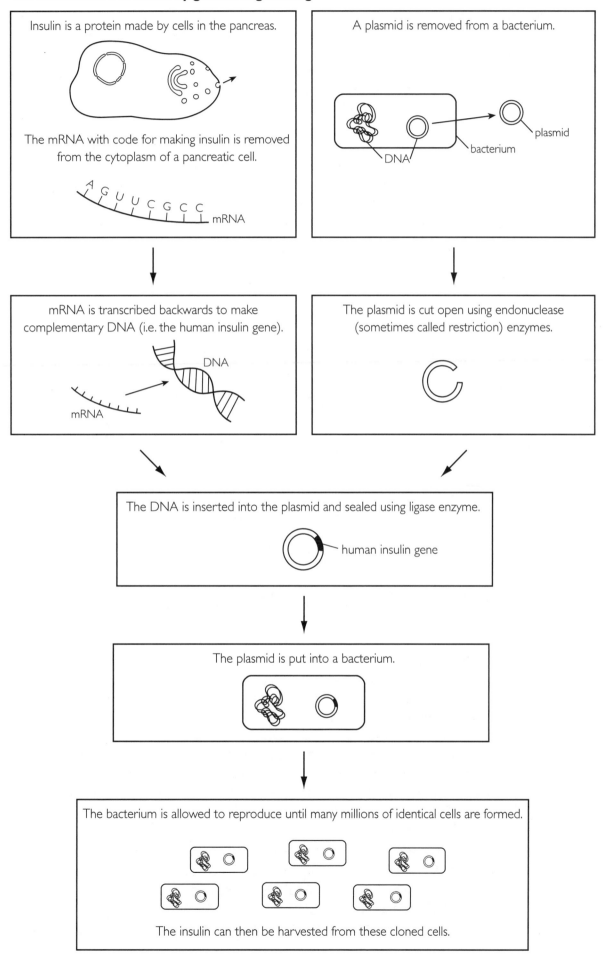

Insulin is a protein made by cells in the pancreas.

The mRNA with code for making insulin is removed from the cytoplasm of a pancreatic cell.

A G U U C G C C — mRNA

A plasmid is removed from a bacterium.

DNA
bacterium
plasmid

mRNA is transcribed backwards to make complementary DNA (i.e. the human insulin gene).

DNA
mRNA

The plasmid is cut open using endonuclease (sometimes called restriction) enzymes.

The DNA is inserted into the plasmid and sealed using ligase enzyme.

human insulin gene

The plasmid is put into a bacterium.

The bacterium is allowed to reproduce until many millions of identical cells are formed.

The insulin can then be harvested from these cloned cells.

Somatic cell fusion

Another technique which allows easy transfer of genes is **somatic cell fusion**. This technique is useful where closely related plant species cannot reproduce sexually. In this procedure, somatic cells (not gametes) from these closely related species of plants are fused. The fusion of cells from quite different parents in any form of reproduction is called **hybridisation** and often results in offspring which are much stronger and healthier. This is sometimes referred to as **hybrid vigour**.

The first problem with somatic cell fusion is the cell wall, which is a tough durable coating made of cellulose. This has to be removed using enzymes such as pectinase and **cellulase**. Once the cell walls have been removed, the cells, called **protoplasts**, have to be treated very carefully, because the membrane can be ruptured easily. So they are kept in an **isotonic solution**. There, when an electric current is applied in a particular way, the plasma membranes can be stimulated to fuse with one another. This allows the nuclei to fuse. The dividing cells form a **callus** which can then be treated with hormones and allowed to develop into a new **polyploid** plant with the combination of the desired features.

Somatic cell fusion

Into the future

The transfer of genes from one organism to another opens up the opportunity to treat human genetic disorders such as muscular dystrophy and cystic fibrosis. The task is to identify the genes which cause the problem and replace them with normal genes, or simply to add the correct genes to the affected cells, so that the correct proteins are made. The hope is, that in the not too distant future, many genetic disorders might be treated in this way. At present only somatic cell therapy is considered, i.e. where only affected tissue is treated. Germline gene therapy involves altering the gene code of the whole organism at a very early stage of development. This has enormous consequences as subsequent generations will inherit the engineered DNA passed on via the sex cells. Gene therapy, particularly if applied to humans, raises serious ethical and moral issues which must first be addressed.

Ethical questions arise from this and other research, which cause heated debate. For example:
1. Where do we draw the line at genetic manipulation of the human genome? If we screen for cystic fibrosis, might we also screen for, and alter, a child's intelligence or even the colour of its hair?
2. Should we grow then destroy human embryos to develop and test treatments for genetic disorders?
3. As the genome of humans becomes easier to determine, should society allow anyone to buy a copy of his or her genome?

(III) ADAPTATION

All living things on the Earth today have many features in common, which is hardly surprising if we accept that Darwin was right, and that we all have a common ancestry. However, one significant feature is the fact that *all* our ancestors, by definition, lived to reproduce offspring. Our ancestry, going back around four billion years, represents in reproductive terms a staggering success story. This achievement was based on adaptability, and in this third part of Unit Two we will look at just a few of the billions of adaptations that have resulted in the almost infinite variety of life we see today.

However, it should not be forgotten that time and evolution move on. Evolution is a dynamic phenomenon; millions of years from now many types of organisms will live on this planet but they will be quite different from those alive today. This will be possible because their ancestors will have adapted to the changing environment, which is our world.

Maintaining a water balance: Animals
Osmoregulation in fish

Fish have gills to breathe. The gills have a very high surface area and are permeable to gases and to water. As a consequence, osmosis takes place across the membranes of the gills. So if a fish does not live in an isotonic environment it will gain or lose water by osmosis.

Bony fish live in either fresh water or in the sea. Fresh water is hypotonic to the body fluids of fish and seawater is hypertonic to the body fluids of fish. Fish with skeletons of cartilage rather than bone (e.g. sharks and rays) have body fluids slightly more concentrated than that of sea water, so even in sea water, they take in a little water by osmosis. *(See page 9.)*

Fresh water fish

Water enters gills by osmosis.

Body fluids are less dilute than surrounding water.

Gills extract salt from water.

Large volume of urine.

Fish living in fresh water gain water by osmosis, so they must get rid of it as fast as it flows into their bodies. To do this they have kidneys with many large glomeruli which filter out the water. However, they lose some salt as a consequence and there is very little salt dissolved in fresh water. So their gills have **chloride secretory cells** which are adapted to actively absorb any salt molecules present in the fresh water. *(See page 9.)*

Bony fish living in the sea have the opposite problem. Paradoxically, they are short of water because it diffuses out of their body constantly, through their gills. To compensate for this loss the fish have to drink sea water. However, the water they drink is too salty, so the excess salt must be removed. Their gills perform the opposite function of their fresh water relatives, and actively pump salts out of their bodies into the sea. Because they are, in effect, short of water, their kidneys contain only a few very small glomeruli and only a small quantity of concentrated urine is produced.

Salt water fish

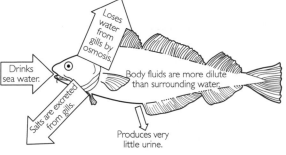

Loses water from gills by osmosis.

Drinks sea water.

Body fluids are more dilute than surrounding water.

Salts are excreted from gills.

Produces very little urine.

Revision of the kidney (See page 60.)

The kidneys filter the blood. In each kidney there are hundreds of thousands of filtering units called nephrons. As the filtered fluid passes through the kidney tubules, water and useful substances are reabsorbed, leaving only nitrogenous waste products (e.g. urea), water and salts to flow into the bladder for storage. Each nephron is composed of a tiny bundle of capillaries surrounded by a capsule into which the filtered fluid flows. Cells and large protein molecules cannot pass through the filter, but most other substances do escape and have to be retrieved. Organisms with plenty of available water have kidneys with many large glomeruli to allow a high filtration rate. Those short of water tend to have fewer and smaller glomeruli in their kidneys and longer loops of Henlé.

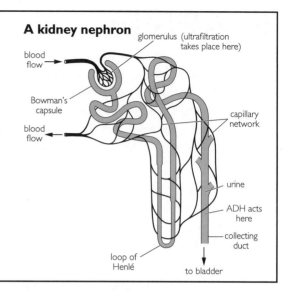

A kidney nephron

Fish which migrate from fresh water to the sea and back again, (e.g. salmon and eels) have to be specially adapted so that they can cope with both environments. Their kidneys can cope with the varied amounts of water available, and their gills have cells which can pump salts in or out of the blood, depending on the osmotic concentration of the water in which they find themselves. Consequently, this adaptation enables salmon to breed in the relative safety of the rivers, and to feed at sea, where there is an abundant supply of food. In contrast, eels breed at sea and return to the rivers to mature.

Water conservation in the desert rat

Animals living in arid deserts clearly have a problem obtaining and retaining water. There are many ways in which they have been adapted, and some adaptations of the desert rat are outlined below. Adaptations can be physiological (functional), anatomical (structural) or behavioural.

Physiological adaptations

Desert rats:

- have high concentrations of ADH (anti-diuretic hormone) in the blood which cause reabsorption of water from the urine (see *page 60*).
- have very dry faeces, because the large intestine is efficient at removing water from undigested food
- do not sweat
- metabolise fat rather than carbohydrate. This results in a greater gain of metabolic water. (Remember that one of the products of aerobic respiration is water.)

Anatomical adaptations

Desert rats:

- have long loops of Henlé in their kidneys, which makes the medulla of the kidney very salty, so increasing the osmotic flow of water out of the urine
- have few, small glomeruli to reduce filtration.

Behavioural adaptations

Desert rats:

- burrow in the sand to avoid the heat of the sun. The burrows are cool and moist, so reducing water loss.
- are nocturnal, i.e. they are active at night, when it is cool and more humid.

Maintaining a water balance: Plants
Transpiration

Plants need water, as do all living things, for a variety of reasons: many chemical reactions take place in water; it is a transport medium; it provides the plant cells with support by cell turgor; it permits gametes to reach one another; and it is one of the raw materials of photosynthesis.

Plants take in water through their roots to fill growing cells and to supply hydrogen for photosynthesis. Unfortunately, from the plants' point of view, water is also lost in large quantities through the leaves by evaporation. This process is called **transpiration** and it occurs because the plant has to expose a large surface area of leaf to the environment to collect sunlight and carbon dioxide. Carbon dioxide gas diffuses into the leaves through tiny pores called **stomata**. Oxygen then diffuses out through the same pores. However, water vapour also escapes from the large surface area of damp cells exposed to the atmosphere. On a hot sunny day this can amount to many litres per hour in a deciduous tree. For this reason, trees and many other flowering plants close their stomata whenever they can, and most commonly during the night when gas exchange is at a minimum. They also have extensive root systems covered in tiny hairs so that there is an enormous surface area through which water can be absorbed. In winter many trees lose their leaves to minimise water loss. It is not all bad news for the plant though. The evaporation of water from the leaves keeps the plant cool in hot sunny conditions, and the water moving up from the soil carries much-needed minerals to the leaves where proteins, nucleic acids, vitamins and chlorophyll are manufactured.

The movement of water from the soil to the leaves is called the **transpiration stream**. The water can be pushed up the stems by root pressure, which is the result of osmosis. In fact, in small plants root pressure can be so great that water droplets are forced out of the end of xylem vessels on humid days. However, water can also be drawn up by the **tension** (pulling force) produced as the water evaporates from the leaves. The tensions are often considerable, but the water columns remain intact because of **cohesion** forces between the water molecules. These forces only come into play because the **xylem vessels** are microscopically small. What is more, xylem vessels are adapted to withstand the great tensions by being reinforced by bands of **lignin**.

The water columns would also collapse if it were not for the strong **adhesion** forces which ensure the water molecules stick to the cellulose fibres of the cell walls in the leaves. We are actually quite familiar with these forces in everyday situations. The cohesive and adhesive properties of water molecules make it difficult to dry clothes, and also explain why blotting paper or tissues absorb water from surfaces so effectively. They also explain the meniscus observed in a narrow measuring cylinder.

The sun provides the heat energy to cause evaporation and pull the water up the plant.

water moves across leaf

Numerous stomata on the leaf can be closed at night to save water.

Water molecules stick to each other and to the sides of the xylem.

one xylem vessel (greatly enlarged)

In humid conditions osmosis forces water up the stems of small plants. This is called 'root pressure'.

Cross section of root

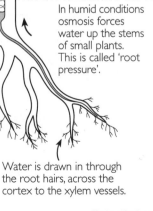

phloem

root hair

xylem

cortex

Water is drawn in through the root hairs, across the cortex to the xylem vessels.

The evaporation of water from a plant is affected by many environmental factors. Changes to the factors listed below all cause an *increase* in the rate of transpiration:

- **decrease in humidity** – less water vapour in the air ensures a greater concentration gradient between the leaf surfaces and the air.
- **increase in wind speed** – water vapour is quickly carried away from near the surface of the leaf to maintain a steep concentration gradient.
- **increase in temperature** – more energy is available to change water from a liquid to a gas.
- **decrease in atmospheric pressure** – the water molecules can escape from the liquid surface more easily, so turning from a liquid state to a gaseous state. Plants on high mountains suffer from this effect.
- **increase in light intensity** – light causes stomata to open, which, indirectly, speeds up transpiration by allowing water vapour to escape more easily. (Note: water vapour = water as a gas)

Transpiration rates can be estimated using a bubble potometer. A stem is attached to a piece of capillary tubing under water. The surfaces of the stem and its leaves are dried and the leaves are allowed to transpire. The movement of water along the capillary tube can be observed by introducing a bubble of air. The time taken for the bubble to travel a particular distance gives an estimate of the rate of transpiration.

Bubble potometer

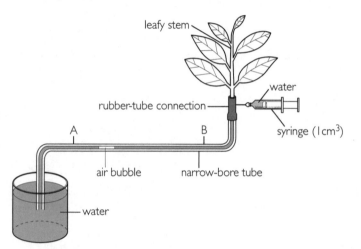

The syringe is used to reset the bubble to position A, so that replicate readings can be taken. Also, the volume of water used can be calculated using the calibrations of the syringe. This volume is not entirely due to transpiration. Some water is taken up by plants to fill growing cells, and some water is required for photolysis.

Stomata

Stomata (singular: stoma) are the pores present on the upper and lower epidermis of leaves of many plants. They are present to allow gas exchange but at the same time to limit water loss. They are usually more numerous on the underside of leaves so that they are less likely to be blocked by dust, and less likely to allow microbes to gain entry to the leaves. Each stoma is surrounded by two guard cells. The guard cells are unusual in two respects: they have chloroplasts (epidermis cells do not normally contain chloroplasts), and they have cell walls which are unevenly thickened. The chloroplasts provide the energy to pump ions by active transport into the guard cells. This results in water flowing into the cells by osmosis. The uneven thickening of the cell walls causes them to bend as the cells become turgid, so opening the pore.

The table below summarises the factors which affect the opening and closing of stomata.

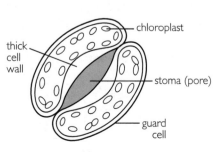

Light conditions	State of guard cells	State of stomata
light	turgid	open
dark	flaccid	closed

Plants show many adaptations to reduce water loss, and plants living in dry places are particularly well adapted to save water. Such plants are called **xerophytes**. Some adaptations are:

- sunken stomata which trap moist air in the sunken pits
- stomata close when there is a shortage of water, because they become flaccid
- thick waxy waterproof cuticles (e.g. heather)
- large water-storing cells (e.g. succulents)
- leaves with a reduced surface area (e.g. spines of cacti)
- leaves which can curl up to trap moist air (e.g. marram grass)
- leaves which are covered in thick hairs to trap moist air
- extensive root systems both deep and shallow
    - deep roots reach the water table many metres below the soil
    - shallow roots make the most of brief rainstorms
- stomata are closed during the day and opened at night, storing carbon dioxide for photosynthesis the following day.

Xerophyte (cactus)   **Cross section through leaf of xerophyte**

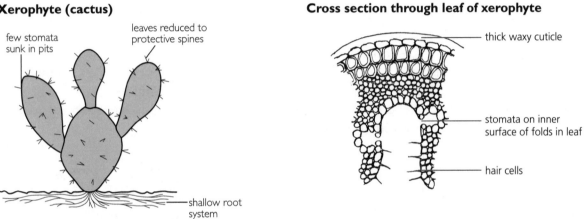

Plants living in fresh water or very wet places are called **hydrophytes**. They have quite different adaptations from xerophytes. Some of these adaptations are:

- reduced xylem because there is no real need for water transport. Any xylem present is found at the centre of the stem rather than at the perimeter. This allows the stems to be flexible rather than rigid.
- small or narrow submerged leaves to reduce damage by water currents (e.g. *Elodea* and water-starwort)
- no stomata on submerged leaves
- stomata on the top surface of floating leaves (e.g. water lily)
- air spaces in the stem and leaves, for buoyancy and to store carbon dioxide and oxygen for the plant.

Hydrophyte (water-starwort)   **Cross section through leaf of hydrophyte**

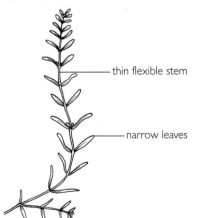
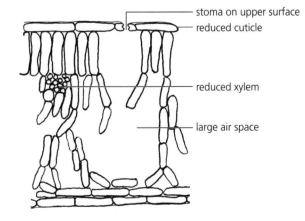

Obtaining food

Animals and plants are profoundly different in the ways in which they obtain food. Plants make their own food by photosynthesis and animals have to obtain their food by eating other animals, or by eating plants. So plants are producers and animals are consumers.

Consequently, most plants have no need to move about and so stay rooted to the same spot – they are **sessile**. Almost all animals, on the other hand, move about to look for and obtain food – they are **mobile**.

Animals

There are almost as many different ways of obtaining food as there are species of animals. Some eat grass; some eat the leaves of trees; others eat fruits or seeds; some eat floating microscopic algae; others eat fish; some eat flying insects and yet others eat the dead or decaying remains of the meals of other animals.

However, there is one feature which is common to all methods of eating, and that is that it must be efficient. In simple terms, the energy expended finding and/or catching the food must be less than the energy gained by eating the food. This is simple economics. Without a surplus of 'income' over 'expenditure', any animal will eventually die. So an animal's behaviour is to a large extent programmed, or pre-wired, to ensure that it is economic in its search for food. Many factors must be taken into account, and it seems that many animals are able to make subconscious decisions as to what strategy to adopt to maximise gain and minimise loss. Such strategies are called **optimal foraging** strategies.

The following considerations might apply to a carnivore of the cat family:

- What time will be spent in finding the prey?
- How much energy will be expended in chasing the prey?
- What time will be spent in killing the prey?
- Is there a risk of injury when trying to overpower and kill the prey?
- How much time will be spent in eating the prey?
- Will other competitors try to steal the prey?
- How nutritious is the prey?
- What is the energy content of the prey?

It must be emphasised that the carnivore does not consider these questions in a rational, conscious way, as we might. Carnivores simply follow a behavioural programme built into their genes which ensures these factors are, to a greater or lesser extent, taken into account while hunting. Genes which favour these strategies are then more likely to survive and be passed on to the next generation. Genes which fail to favour these strategies are likely to disappear, along with their owner, long before they have an opportunity to be passed on to the next generation.

Such optimal strategies apply to any animal, not just carnivores. So, herbivores will select particular plants to eat, and may time migration or hibernation to minimise energy loss and maximise energy gain.

In any situation there is also another factor which always affects the success of an animal in obtaining food, and that is **competition**. This competition can be **interspecific** or **intraspecific**. In the former, animals of *one species* compete with animals of *another species* for food. In the latter, animals compete with other animals of the *same species*. In some cases, there may appear to be co-operation rather than competition. For example, this can be seen in the activities of dolphins in rounding up a shoal of fish to catch and eat, or in the social interactions of ants or bees. However, underlying even these apparently co-operative behaviours lies a basic selfish drive to ensure survival.

Interspecific competition

Even at the level of micro-organisms there is conflict between species for scarce resources. Fungi and bacteria both feed on dead and decaying material in the soil. So, to reduce competition from bacteria, fungi produce antibiotics, such as penicillin, to keep bacteria at bay. Humans now use micro-organisms to produce antibiotics on a grand scale for treating bacterial diseases.

If two different species of organism compete for the same food in the same ecosystem, then almost invariably one of the two species will lose and disappear from the area of competition — at worst it will become extinct. So, the only strategy to avoid extinction is to occupy a **niche** (to have a life-style and diet) which is different, even if only slightly so, from that of any other species sharing the same ecosystem. In short, species have to specialise. If they don't, the ensuing competition for resources will eventually eliminate the weaker competitor. So, very often, when it appears that two different species are feeding on the same food, this will not be the case. For example, on the plains of Africa, the gazelles, the zebras and the wildebeest all eat grass, but there are subtle differences in where, when and what grass is eaten. This has been verified by observation and by examining the contents of the stomachs and faeces of these herbivores. The zebra's digestive system is inefficient, but it makes up for this by eating large quantities of coarse long grass rather quickly. Its jaws are adapted for this because they have strong incisors. When the zebras crop the long coarse grass, new shoots are stimulated to grow. The wildebeest can then select these new younger shoots, whereas the gazelles actually eat quite a high proportion of dicotyledons (broad-leaved plants), which can grow more easily once the tall grasses have been cropped.

Wading birds which feed on the mudflats near the sea might appear to be seeking the same food, but in fact knots, redshanks and curlews all have different lengths and shapes of beak to seek different food items at different depths in the mud.

Intraspecific competition

Unlike interspecific competition, intraspecific competition is inevitable because members of the same species, by definition, occupy the same niche and eat the same food. What is more, there will almost invariably be competition for the best mate and/or the most suitable territory. So all kinds of strategies are adopted to ensure success, yet minimise the risk of injury and energy loss.

Dominance hierarchy

In many social mammal groups (e.g. baboons) all the members, particularly the males, have rank positions which relate to their age, strength and social skills. There is conflict between the members of the group to attempt to move up the rank order, but these conflicts are often carried out in such a way that there is little or no risk of injury. Signs and signals of strength and vigour are often sufficient to deter outright attack and very often such signals are the submissive ones of lower ranked individuals, rather than the **threat displays** of higher ranked animals. The same is true in some bird species, including the common farmyard hen, where social groups establish a '**pecking order**'. The high-ranking individuals clearly have the best of everything – food and mates – but the low-ranking individuals sometimes gain enough to make it more worthwhile to be part of the group than to live in solitude. For example, there is a degree of protection from predators and there are opportunities to mate, albeit few and far between, but this is much better than having no opportunity to mate at all. In a pride of lions, even the lowest-ranking individual will obtain some food from the kill and the chances of catching and killing prey are enhanced by the co-operative hunting techniques employed by the pride.

dominant posture

submissive posture

Co-operative hunting

Co-operative hunting requires an ability to communicate and co-operate on a sophisticated level.
There are many advantages to be gained from co-operative hunting:
* Larger prey can be tackled.
* Prey can be found more easily.
* Prey can be caught more easily by ambush, by creating confusion or by surrounding it.
* Prey can be kept more easily from other predators or scavengers.

The principal disadvantage of co-operative hunting is that any prey caught has to be shared to a greater or lesser extent. A solitary cheetah catching a gazelle gets to eat the entire prey, if it so wishes, whereas a lion must share its prey with other members of the pride.

Dolphins provide a good example of co-operative hunters. They are highly intelligent and have a sophisticated communication system. Moreover, they use sonar to detect their prey. Pulses of sound are sent out, and bounce back from objects in the water. In this way, shoals of fish can be detected. By working in groups dolphins can substantially increase the width of the sonar search beam. Once a shoal of fish is detected, the dolphins work together to bring the shoal to the surface where the fish form a tight, swirling 'baitball'. This behaviour by the fish is in itself a method of protection. The chances of being eaten are reduced if you share a shoal with hundreds or thousands of other fish. What is more the swirling and flashing movement of the shoal can bemuse and bewilder a predator. However, the dolphins themselves cause confusion in the shoal by making loud clicking noises and by blowing bubbles of air up from below. Any fish which panic are then picked off as they try to escape from the baitball. Dolphins are such successful hunters that opportunistic carnivores such as sharks and tuna will follow a herd of dolphins to take advantage of their superior hunting skills.

Territorial behaviour

One very effective way to reduce intraspecific competition is to maintain a territory from where other members of the same species are excluded. Since space is always in short supply, conflict is inevitable, but the risks of injury and the energy expended can be reduced by marking out the territory in a variety of simple ways. For example, many garden birds will maintain a territory primarily by display and by song. Many carnivores will maintain a territory by sound and scent signals, e.g. lions will roar and also urinate at various points round the perimeter of their territory to advertise their presence. This is a low cost and low risk strategy that works most of the time. However, the defence of all territory must inevitably involve aggressive threat displays of one kind or another, and can result in serious fighting if the threat displays indicate there is little or no difference in the strength and fitness of the antagonists.

Territories can be different sizes, depending on their purpose, and many vertebrate (back-boned) animals maintain territories of one kind or another. At the simplest level, gulls only need a territory of a few square decimetres, just enough to build a nest. They feed at sea where it is impossible to mark out a territory on the featureless expanse of water. Robins, on the other hand, will defend a territory the size of a small garden by singing and by aggressive display of their red breasts. This territory will be big enough to attract a mate, to build a nest and to provide sufficient area to search for insects and grubs to feed the growing young.

Stickleback

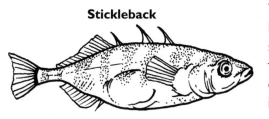

The genetic programme which dictates territorial behaviour can be very simple. For example, in the breeding season, sticklebacks, like robins, respond aggressively to the presence of a red patch on the underside of a male competitor. In one famous experiment with sticklebacks, it was discovered that the males in the breeding season responded even to the passage of a red Post Office van outside the window in which their tank was situated!

Obtaining food: Plants

Plants make their own food using the energy of the sun and two very simple and easily obtainable raw materials. However, they also need tiny quantities of minerals from the soil to turn glucose and other compounds from the Calvin cycle into complex organic compounds such as ATP, proteins, nucleic acids and vitamins.

Because plants make their own food, they have no need to search for it in the way that animals do, so most are **sessile** – they remain fixed to one spot. This implies that they don't move at all, but they do. Speeded-up film shows that plants move quite considerable distances in their search for light, water and nutrients. Their roots spread through the soil and their stems can grow to considerable lengths to gain access to the best light. Because the movements are so slow, however, we are inclined not to realise that in a jungle or even a grassy plain there is intense inter and intraspecific competition between plants for water, minerals and light.

One adaptation which has evolved in plants, particularly those living in forests, is the ability to grow in low light intensities. Earlier (*see page 10*) you learned that plants have a wide range of pigments in their leaves to make the best use of available light. Some also have mechanisms to enable them to make use of weak light. In fact direct sunlight can damage some shade-loving plants, as you will know if you have put certain species of house plants in an unprotected greenhouse.

Compensation point

The ability of a plant to grow in poor light is dependent upon its **compensation point**. This is the light intensity at which rates of growth are zero because the plant is photosynthesising and respiring at the same rate. In light intensities greater than this, plants can grow because they can make more glucose by photosynthesis than is used by respiration. At compensation point, gas exchange is balanced. The volume of carbon dioxide taken up equals the volume of carbon dioxide released, and similarly with oxygen. Plants adapted to growing in full sunlight (**sun plants**) have compensation points at relatively high light intensities, whereas **shade plants** have compensation points at low light intensities.

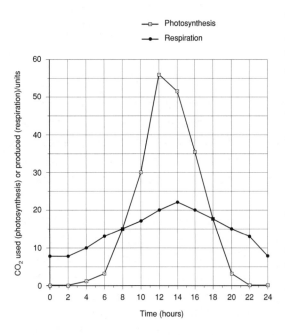

This graph shows the rates of respiration and photosynthesis in a plant, over a 24 hour period. The compensation points are at 8 hours and 18 hours. The greatest net productivity is at noon.

The term 'compensation point' can also be applied to ecosystems, or even to the Earth as a whole. If all the photosynthesis and respiration taking place on the planet is in balance then we would be at compensation point. Unfortunately, at present this is not the case, because we are producing more carbon dioxide than is being used up by photosynthesis. This is because we are burning vast quantities of fossil fuels and cutting down the forests of the world. The excess carbon dioxide in the atmosphere, along with a number of other polluting gases, appears to be having an effect on our climate. This effect is often referred to as 'global warming' or the 'greenhouse effect'.

Light is not the only factor to affect rates of photosynthesis. Low carbon dioxide concentrations and temperature can also limit rates of photosynthesis, and at any point in time, only one of these factors will limit the rate. For example, on a hot sunny day in a tropical rainforest, it is very likely that insufficient carbon dioxide will limit rates of photosynthesis.

Coping with danger: Animals
Individual defence mechanisms

As a consequence of competition and predation in all its forms, many different mechanisms to cope with danger have evolved in animals. For example, they may:

- be fast runners, fliers or swimmers
- be well camouflaged
- feign death
- have startling displays of colour or shape
- be poisonous to eat
- have a poisonous sting or bite
- make warning sounds
- mimic other more dangerous animals
- be very good at learning.

Learning

One adaptation for survival is the ability to learn from experience. Evolution has favoured this ability in many animals, and humans provide the best example of animals who can learn. For us, there is so much to learn that we take many years to reach maturity. This is costly in the economics of survival. What is more, learning is only of value if the mistakes you make don't result in your death before you have had time to learn from them!

A few examples of learned behaviour are given below.
1. Reindeer learn to paw away snow to reach green shoots below.
2. Rats learn where the best supply of food can be found in a farmyard.
3. Chimpanzees learn to use sticks to prise out insects and grubs from rotten logs.
4. Rabbits learn not to eat nettles because they sting.
5. Frogs learn not to eat flying insects with black and yellow stripes because they sting.
6. Snails learn not to respond to a tap on the shell, if the tap is not followed by an event of any kind.

Examples **4** and **5** are examples of **avoidance behaviours**, as would be **6** if the snail had retreated into its shell. However, example **6** is an example of **habituation**. This is a temporary behaviour where an animal *ceases* to respond to a stimulus so long as it provides no reward and no punishment. Habituation has survival value, because energy is saved in *not* responding to events which are of no consequence.

Social defence mechanisms

All animals interact with others of the same species but some do so in social groups for periods of time. As for any form of behaviour there are both costs and benefits.

Examples of costs	Examples of benefits
Disease spreads more easily.	There is greater protection from predators.
Food has to be shared.	Mates can be found more easily.

One of the major benefits is that of defence against predators. For example, in a group of feeding animals (e.g. a flock of birds):

* there are many pairs of eyes to watch for predators
* only one alarm call is needed to warn all the members of the group
* all members of the group can spend more time feeding
* predators can be mobbed and scared away by aggressive group behaviour (e.g. troops of baboons will scare away big cats in this way)
* predators can be startled and confused by rapid co-ordinated group movements (e.g. shoals of fish or flocks of birds – see *page 45*). Flocks or shoals can tighten up and swirl around rapidly so that an attacker is confused and has less chance of catching any individual.

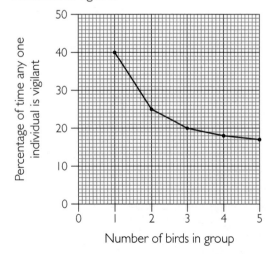 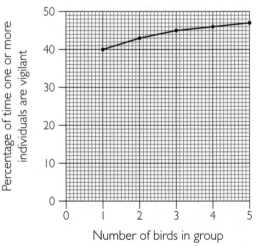

Flock changes flight pattern on appearance of predatory hawk.

Ostriches move about in herds for part of their lives. When feeding, there is always a need for one or more individuals to raise their heads and keep watch for predators. What conclusions about this vigilance behaviour can be drawn from the two graphs below? (*The answers are at the back of the book.*)

Graph 1 shows the percentage of time any one individual is vigilant.

Graph 2 shows the percentage of time one or more individuals (i.e. the group) is vigilant.

Coping with danger: Plants

Plants are also in constant competition with herbivores and have developed all kinds of strategies to defend themselves. Some of these at cellular and chemical level have been described previously (*see page 19*) but some examples of structural adaptations are shown below.

The effects of grazing on plant diversity

Grazing by herbivores can have a variety of effects on the diversity and numbers of plants growing in a particular area. Much depends on the kind of plant the animal chooses to eat and on interspecific competition between the plants. Grazing can reduce species diversity if less vigorous plants are selected by herbivores. The vast tracts of moorland in Scotland have rather low species diversity and are kept from reaching their natural **climax community** status (*see page 63*), with all its rich diversity of trees and shrubs, by the activities of sheep and deer. On the other hand, in some situations, if the dominant species of plant is removed, this allows other less robust plants to colonise an area and species diversity can increase.

Toleration of grazing

Plants are adapted to tolerate grazing in a variety of different ways.

Grasses, which are monocotyledonous (narrow-leaved) plants, have **meristems** (growing points where cells divide) at or below ground level. So when the leaves are cropped off by the grazers, new growth can still take place from ground level.

Dicotyledonous (broad-leaved) plants have different adaptations. Their growing points are often well above ground. However, when a leading shoot is removed, a hormonal change stimulates buds lower in the stem to sprout. (*See page 52.*)

Plantain

rosette of leaves

Some dicotyledonous plants (dicots) have what is called a rosette habit, i.e. they grow very close to the ground, with their leaves pressed flat to the surface, so that herbivores have difficulty actually getting their teeth below them to nip them off. For example, many species of dicots found on lawns survive in this way, e.g. plantain. A lawnmower is not much different from a herbivore in this respect!

Stinging nettle

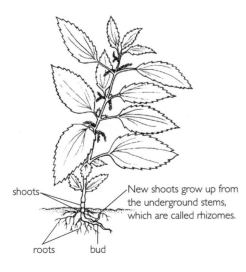

shoots

New shoots grow up from the underground stems, which are called rhizomes.

roots   bud

Many plants protect themselves from herbivores by having stings, thorns or spines. Cacti are probably the best known of these, but there are many other examples of plants with this form of defence nearer to home, such as hawthorn, holly, bramble, gorse and stinging nettle. Nettles also have underground stems (rhizomes) from which new shoots can regenerate, even if all the stems above ground are damaged by fire or by herbivores. This makes plants such as nettles and couch grass particularly difficult for gardeners and farmers to eradicate.

Interestingly, new holly leaves are succulent and soft before their spines become hard. Consequently they are attractive to herbivores. So one can often find stunted holly trees in deciduous woodland, unable to grow properly because of the attention of deer.

UNIT THREE — CONTROL AND REGULATION

This 40-hour unit contains information on the control of growth in plants and animals, the influences of hormones and of the environment, physiological homeostasis and population dynamics.

Growth and development

In flowering plants growth and development starts in regions called **meristems** where cell division takes place. In animals, cell division tends not to be localised in this fashion. In a growing plant the principal meristems are found at the tips of the stems and roots, hence they are called **apical meristems** (apex – tip). In these meristems there is active **DNA replication**, **mitosis** (*see page 53*)and **cell division**. After the cells have divided, many increase in size due to the formation of vacuoles. As each cell increases in size, so roots and shoots grow longer and leaves expand.

Following vacuolation many cells become specialised to carry out particular functions: epidermis cells form to protect the plant, xylem vessels carry water and minerals and support the plant, root hairs increase the surface area for absorption, and mesophyll cells carry out photosynthesis. This process of specialisation is sometimes called **differentiation**.

So growth takes place as a result of three processes:
1. increase in cell number
2. increase in cell size
3. increase in cell specialisation.

As a plant grows in length it also needs to grow in girth. A cylinder of meristematic (dividing) cells, called the **cambium**, forms inside the stem and root of the plant. In perennials (plants which grow for more than one year) the cambium cells start to divide actively every spring. Xylem tissue is formed on the inside and phloem tissue on the outside. Each year, as the buds break dormancy and new leaves grow, large xylem vessels are required to supply them with water. However, by the summer, only smaller xylem vessels are produced to supply the additional leaves which grow on new twigs. In the autumn and winter, cambium activity ceases. As a consequence, cylinders of spring (wide bore) and summer (narrow bore) xylem vessels form each year. If a cut is made across a tree trunk it is possible to see rings

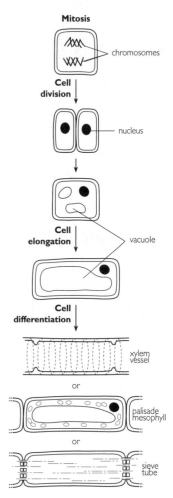

of spring and summer wood, and the age of a tree can be easily determined by counting these annual rings which form the grain of the wood. Annual rings are most pronounced in trees and shrubs which grow in temperate regions (*see diagram of the Earth on page 59*) of the world, where there is a greater difference in climate between summer and winter. Tropical hardwoods, such as mahogany and teak, are less grained. Rings of phloem are also produced each year but these soft living cells, which make up part of the bark, are compressed and die at the end of each year, so there are no annual rings of phloem.

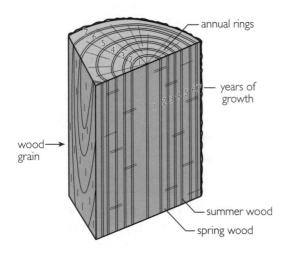

Cross section of a three-year-old stem

Cell detail of an annual ring to show spring and summer wood

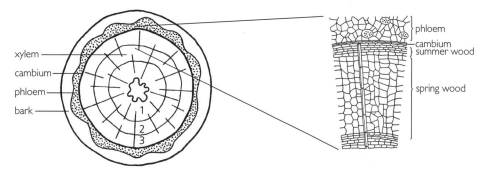

Growth patterns

Growth can be measured by an increase in the number of cells, length, volume or mass. Dry mass is a more accurate measure of growth, as the mass of water in an organism can vary considerably. However, there is a major drawback to measuring the dry mass of an organism: it has to be killed. The graphs below show the growth curves for an annual plant (e.g. cress), a perennial plant (e.g. oak tree), a locust and a human.

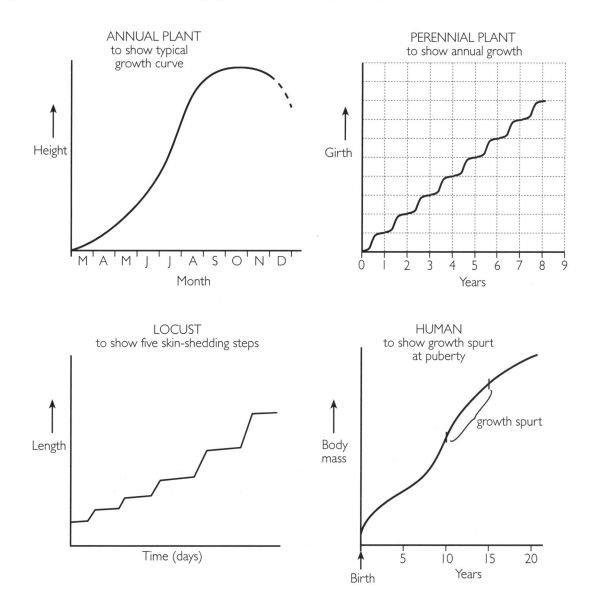

Regeneration

Regeneration is the process by which an organism regains its normal form after damage or fragmentation of one kind or another. Animals have some ability to regenerate tissues. For example, tadpoles and many lizards can replace a lost tail with one almost identical to the original. Salamanders can replace lost legs, and many sponges can re-form after being completely fragmented by being forced through a sieve! For simple animals, such as sponges, this process is a useful method of asexual reproduction, as small fragments, broken off by accident, can re-form new genetically identical individuals. However, regeneration in mammals is limited to only a few tissues. For example, red blood cells, liver cells and skin and bone tissue can all regenerate to replace lost or damaged cells, but arms and legs cannot re-grow. Nervous tissue, for example, has very poor powers of regeneration, so people with damaged spinal cords are likely to remain paralysed for the rest of their lives.

In contrast, a plant's ability to regenerate tissue with ease is of great value to plant breeders. A tiny fragment of leaf, stem or root can be treated with hormones so that it develops into a new plant, genetically identical to the original plant. In this way, if a new, desirable variety is produced by selective breeding, many identical individuals (a **clone**) can then be produced very quickly and easily.

Micro-propagation

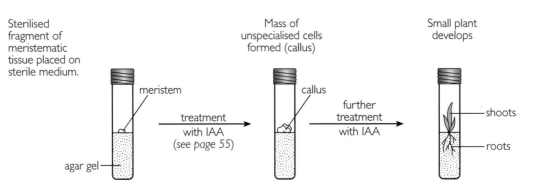

The power of regeneration confirms that somatic (body) cells of plants and animals all possess a complete set of genes. All that is required for regeneration is the right conditions to switch the appropriate genes on and off.

When plants are damaged, for example, when they are eaten by herbivores, they are usually able to regenerate their lost parts. **Dicotyledons** (broad-leaved plants) tend to have their growing points at the ends of their shoots. When these are removed the plant simply responds by starting growth again further down the stem where there are many potential new shoots. These shoots are normally held in check by **auxins** (plant hormones) produced by the apical meristem. (See page 55.) When this dominant apical meristem is removed, new side shoots are then free to develop. This principle is used by house plant growers. They cut off the leading shoots and this encourages new bushy growth further down the stem. When a hedge is cut, many new shoots replace the lost leading shoots and the hedge becomes thicker and more attractive.

Monocotyledons (narrow-leaved plants, e.g. grasses – see page 49) solve the problem of grazing in a different way. They have their meristems at the bases of their leaves so that as the leaves are removed, the meristems remain intact at ground level. This is a very effective way for plants to survive grazing and this is why grasses are the most abundant plants to grow on heavily grazed ground. Grass lawns provide an excellent example of the effectiveness of this form of regeneration.

Genetic control

Every organism starts off life as a single cell – a **zygote**. In multicellular organisms the zygote goes on to divide, and many divisions later, the adult organism is formed. Each **cell division** is preceded by a process of **nuclear division** called **mitosis**. This process ensures that each cell has a perfect copy of the DNA of that particular organism.

During mitosis, the chromosomes shorten and thicken and appear as identical pairs of chromatids. These chromatids are the result of earlier DNA replication. The nuclear membrane disappears and the chromosomes migrate to the middle (**equator**) of the cell. Unlike meiosis, they do not pair up. Instead, each chromatid becomes linked to a spindle fibre which then pulls the chromatid apart from its neighbour. (*See page 50.*) When the two sets of chromatids reach the poles of the cell, they uncoil and become chromosomes again; the nuclear membrane re-forms and the cell goes on to divide.

If every cell has an identical set of genetic instructions in its DNA, how then do cells differentiate into blood cells, nerve cells, bone cells, mesophyll cells, cortex cells and root hair cells? The answer lies in a switching mechanism. As cells develop, the required genes are switched on and off in the correct sequence. This process is still by and large a mystery, which scientists are trying to resolve. However, the solution will help find the cure for many of the genetic disorders which affect our lives. For example, the breakdown of this control mechanism results in balls of cells of different types (tumours) growing in an uncontrolled way; a condition we call cancer.

Two scientists, **Jacob** and **Monod**, showed how this control mechanism works in the bacterium *Escherichia coli*. The bacterium digests **lactose** to obtain glucose, using an enzyme called **galactosidase**. However, it only makes the enzyme when it is required, thus saving valuable energy and resources. The synthesis of the enzyme is controlled by a gene switch.

Three genes are involved:

Gene	Function
structural gene	codes for **galactosidase**
operator*	switches on structural gene
regulator gene	codes for a **repressor** molecule

*Strictly speaking, the operator is not a gene, because it does not code for a protein but acts only as a gene switch. When lactose is absent the operator switch is kept 'OFF' by the presence of a molecule (called a **repressor**) which binds to it. The repressor is produced by the **regulator gene**.

However, when lactose is present, the lactose binds to the repressor molecule and stops it working. Therefore the repressor cannot switch the operator off and the enzyme is then synthesised. Here the lactose is called an **inducer** because it triggers the manufacture of the enzyme. However, once the lactose has been digested, the **repressor molecule** becomes functional again and the enzyme is no longer made.

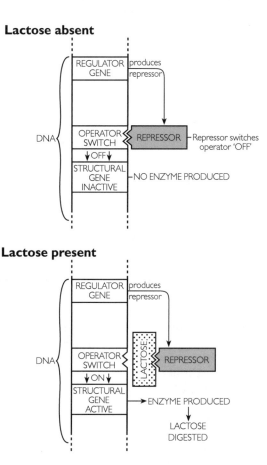

Lactose absent

Lactose present

Phenylketonuria

When a mutation occurs, the common result is for an enzyme to be improperly manufactured, or even absent. In such cases a **metabolic pathway** is blocked and very often the effect can be lethal. For example, the absence of the enzyme which converts the amino acid **phenylalanine** to the amino acid **tyrosine** results in a condition called **phenylketonuria (PKU)**. This condition is caused by a recessive allele, so both parents must be carriers of the allele before any child can be affected. The disorder can be fatal if not treated.

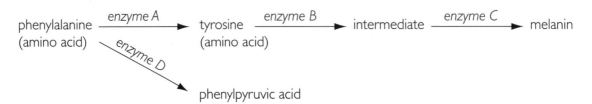

Without *enzyme A* phenylalanine accumulates in the blood and some of it is converted to phenylpyruvic acid, which is excreted in the urine. The excess of both compounds disrupts the normal development of various organs, including the brain. Fortunately, there is now a blood test which can be carried out at birth to check for this condition, and children suffering from PKU are given a low phenylalanine diet for a number of years until their brains are fully developed.

Sufferers of PKU also have lighter hair and lighter skins because they can only make melanin from tyrosine and not from phenylalanine. Melanin is the brown pigment which colours skin and hair. Tyrosine, an amino acid, is obtained in any normal balanced diet, as are all other amino acids. An absence of *enzyme C* would result in a condition called albinism, where no pigmentation is produced.

Hormone influences

Hormones are chemicals produced in tiny quantities at one site in an organism, which then affect other parts of the organism. In animals, hormones are carried in the blood; in plants, hormones diffuse from cell to cell and are also transported by the phloem.

Humans

Hormones have a profound effect on the growth and development of humans. For example, during a brief period of early life in the womb, a gene on the Y-chromosome (if this chromosome is present) switches on the production of the hormone testosterone. This hormone alters the developmental processes taking place so that the foetus becomes a male rather than a female.

Growth of humans is controlled by a number of hormones other than testosterone. Three other hormones which have a profound influence on growth are shown in the table below.

Hormone	Produced by	Effect
human growth hormone (HGH)	pituitary gland (under brain)	stimulates protein synthesis and the growth of bones
thyroid stimulating hormone (TSH)	pituitary gland	stimulates the thyroid gland to produce thyroxine
thyroxine	thyroid gland (in neck)	stimulates metabolic rate (chemical reactions in the cells)

Individuals lacking sufficient HGH do not grow to full height.

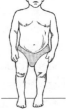

Plants

Many chemical substances affect the growth of plants. Most act like hormones, but are sometimes called **plant growth substances**.

Two such groups of substances are **auxins** and **gibberellins**. Both substances are produced by meristematic (dividing) cells in shoots, roots or leaves of plants, and each influences growth and development in a variety of ways.

Indole acetic acid (IAA) is the most common auxin and it is synthesised by meristematic cells. The graph shows the effect of different concentrations of IAA on the growth of roots, stems and flowers of an angiosperm (flowering plant).

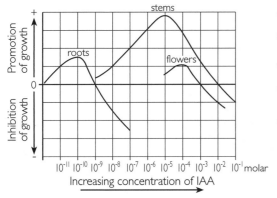

What effect does IAA at a concentration of 10^{-8} molar have on the growth of roots and stems?

What effect does IAA at a concentration of 10^{-3} molar have on the growth of flowers and stems?

(The answers are at the back of the book.)

- In growing shoots IAA promotes cell elongation. When shoots are lit from one side, auxin moves to the shaded side and causes it to grow more than on the lit side. This makes the shoot bend towards the light and this growth movement is called **positive phototropism**.

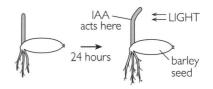

- In cambium tissues (*see page 50*) IAA promotes cell division and cell differentiation.

- The presence of IAA in the stem of many plants inhibits the growth of lateral buds. (*See page 52.*) So if the apical bud is removed from a shoot, by a herbivore for example, the lateral buds will start to develop. This is a useful adaptation, because the damage to the apical shoot stimulates the growth of new shoots further down the stem.

- In the autumn, a drop in the concentration of IAA stimulates leaf **abscission** (leaf drop).

- IAA plays a part in the development of seeds and fruits. So fruit growers use the hormone to stimulate the growth of fruits, such as grapes, without seeds.

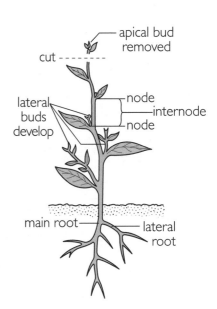

- IAA is used by horticulturalists to stimulate root growth in cuttings. It is also used as a selective herbicide (weedkiller) on grass, where it kills broad-leaved plants such as dandelions, but not the grass.

Gibberellic acid (**GA$_3$**) is the most common of the gibberellins. Like auxins it stimulates the division and growth of cells, but it plays no part in phototropic movements.

- It acts as a gene switch to make dwarf varieties of plants grow tall. For example, in Mendel's pea plants, the dwarf variety lacks GA$_3$.
- GA$_3$ plays a role in the germination of seeds. Seeds remain dormant until they have experienced certain conditions, e.g. a cold spell or a period of drought. So GA$_3$ can be used as a substitute for these factors to stimulate the germination of barley, for example, by brewers.
- In barley and other grasses the embryo produces GA$_3$ which causes the **aleurone layer** – a layer of metabolically active cells in the **endosperm** – to produce **α-amylase**. This enzyme digests the starch stored in the endosperm to release the sugar maltose which can then be used by the germinating grain. Here, the GA$_3$ is acting as a gene switch to switch on the gene which codes for α-amylase.

Barley grain (longitudinal section)

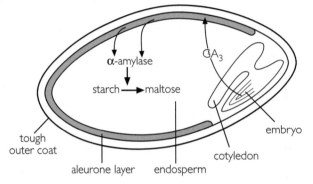

Action of plant growth substances

Location	Role of IAA
shoot tip	stimulates cell division and elongation

Location	Role of IAA
ovary of fertilised flower	stimulates development of fruit

Location	Role of IAA
lateral bud	inhibits development of bud

Location	Role of GA$_3$
internode	stimulates cell elongation

Plant mineral requirements

Green plants are unique in life on Earth because they can make their own complex organic compounds using the simplest of ingredients. It is often said that plants make their own food from carbon dioxide and water using the energy of sunlight. However, this is not quite the whole story. To make complex molecules such as proteins, nucleic acids and vitamins, plants need a supply of nitrogen and a number of other mineral elements. These are found dissolved in soil water which is absorbed by plant roots. These minerals are then combined with carbohydrates, produced during photosynthesis, to form the myriads of complex compounds which go to make up the entire plant.

Plants are able to actively select and absorb these elements against concentration gradients, using the energy provided by ATP. (See page 9.)

The major elements required by plants apart from carbon, hydrogen and oxygen are nitrogen (N), phosphorus (P), potassium (K) and magnesium (Mg).
- Nitrogen is required for the manufacture of amino acids, nucleic acids and chlorophyll.
- Phosphorus is required for the manufacture of ATP, RNA, DNA, GP and RuBP.
- Magnesium is required for the manufacture of chlorophyll.
- Potassium is important in membrane transport.

It is possible to find out how lack of any one of these minerals affects plant growth by growing the plants in different solutions of minerals. Containers are filled with experimental solutions as follows: one is set up with a supply of all the minerals, and the rest are set up lacking one mineral each. Container A is described as a **control**. A control is used for comparison, to prove that any changes which occur in the experiment are actually caused by the factor which is being investigated.

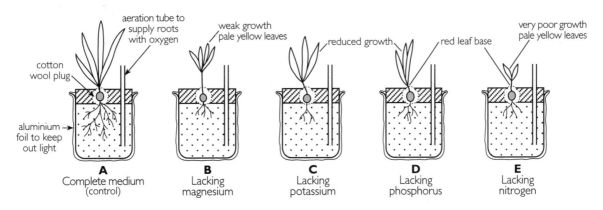

Seedlings are germinated and then suspended in each of the culture solutions. Seedlings with small cotyledons or endosperms are selected because they store fewer minerals and are more likely to be affected by a lack of minerals in the surrounding water. Light is excluded from the solutions to prevent algal growth. The algae would use up the minerals and upset the carefully controlled balance. All other variables, such as temperature, pH, concentration of minerals in solution, volume of solution, duration of experiment and type of seed, are kept constant. This is very important because if two factors are changed then it is impossible to tell which factor has affected the growth of the plant and the results of the investigation would therefore be **invalid**. To ensure the results of the experiment are **reliable**, a number of **replicates** (repeats) should be set up. Growth of seedlings can be measured in a variety of ways: e.g. length of leaves, number of leaves, length of roots and dry mass of plant. Leaves unable to develop chlorophyll appear pale yellow in colour and are said to be **chlorotic**.

The influence of diet on animal growth

Animals are no different from plants in their need for minerals in their diet. However, they obtain their minerals in the food they eat. For example, **iron** is needed for the manufacture of **haemoglobin**. Haemoglobin is the protein found in red blood cells. Red blood cells have little else but this protein in them; they have no nucleus and few organelles. As a consequence their lifespan is only a few months. However, the body manufactures around two million of them every second, so there is rarely a shortage! As haemoglobin combines with and releases oxygen very readily, it is an ideal compound for the transport of oxygen. Iron is also found in the carrier proteins of the **cytochrome chain** of respiration. There the iron is reduced and oxidised in turn as electrons are transferred from one cytochrome to the next. (See *page 14.*)

Many minerals and vitamins are essential in the diet as they act as **cofactors** to **enzymes**. These are substances which are needed for the enzyme to function properly. Metals such as zinc, iron, and copper work in this way. If the diet is deficient in minerals or vitamins, disease results.

Rickets

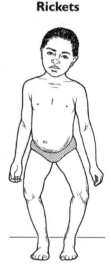

Calcium is another mineral element which is absolutely essential in the diet. An average person needs around a gram of calcium in his or her diet every day, and this is best obtained from milk or milk products. However, calcium ions cannot be absorbed from the food in the intestine unless **vitamin D** is present. If this vitamin is absent then growing children can suffer from **rickets**, a condition in which the bones do not form properly. Shells, bones and teeth all contain a high proportion of calcium, and calcium is also needed for the clotting of blood and for the proper functioning of nerves and muscles.

However, an excess of some substances can have the opposite effect on enzyme activity; the activity is then inhibited rather than promoted. Many well-known poisons work in this way: e.g. DDT (an insecticide), antibiotics and cyanide. (See *page 19.*) These are called enzyme **inhibitors**. **Lead**, which was once used in the manufacture of paint, water pipes and petrol, is a good example of an enzyme inhibitor. However, because it is toxic, its use is now banned.

Fancy a fag?

No thanks!

Substances such as **alcohol** and **nicotine** are particularly harmful to the developing foetus. Women who smoke or drink large quantities of alcohol during pregnancy can cause brain damage to their child and retard its growth. The drug **thalidomide**, which was given to pregnant women in the 1960s to treat morning sickness, was found to seriously inhibit limb formation of unborn children.

Light and its effect on plants and animals

Light influences animals and plants in numerous ways. For example, the direction of light and the duration of light can influence both growth and behaviour.

Plants

Deprived of light, a plant will die because it cannot photosynthesise. But light affects plants in many other ways: for example, it is needed for the synthesis of chlorophyll. Plants grown in the dark produce poorly developed, yellow leaves and long stems. This response to lack of light is called **etiolation** and gives the plant the best chance to reach light by directing all its efforts to increasing stem length.

Many plants respond to the direction of the rays of light. Their stems grow towards the light and their leaves grow at right angles to the light to present a maximum surface area for photosynthesis. This is called **phototropism**. (*See page 55.*)

Etiolated plant

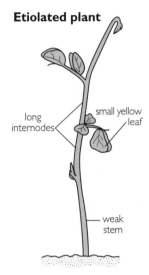

long internodes

small yellow leaf

weak stem

Climatic regions of the Earth
on 21st December

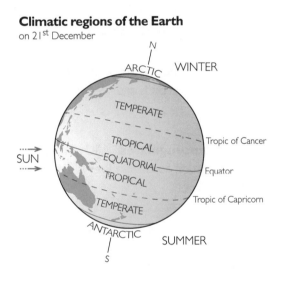

Plants have also adapted their flowering times to coincide with the best conditions for pollination, seed formation and germination. Many use the changing length of day to time these events and this phenomenon is called **photoperiodism**. Changes to the length of day are very precise, and result from the permanent tilt of the Earth's axis as it revolves on its orbit round the sun. Differences are greatest at the poles and least at the equator. Consequently, most plants living in temperate regions flower in the spring, as day length increases and temperatures rise. Some, living nearer the equator, flower as day length decreases, perhaps because pollinating insects are more common or because the rainy season coincides with that time of the year.

Plants which start to flower when day length becomes greater than a critical value are called **long-day plants**, and those which start to flower when day length becomes less than a critical value are **short-day plants**. So a long-day plant might start to flower when day length is greater than 10 hours and a short-day plant might start to flower when day length becomes less than 11 hours! Those plants which do not respond to day length are called **day-neutral plants**.

At first it was thought that it was the length of exposure to light which was critical, but now it is known that the length of the dark period is more important. So, for example, long-day plants actually flower when night length becomes less than a critical period. Just how this happens, no one is as yet quite sure. Certainly, a detection system is required and hormones are involved.

Animals

Some animals respond to changes in day length to time events such as breeding, hibernation and migration. Changes in temperature can also influence these behaviours, but climatic changes are more variable and are a less reliable measure of the passage of time.

For example, it is important that young are born when it is warm and there is an ample supply of food. Mating in large mammals such as deer occurs in the autumn so that fawns are born in the spring. Smaller mammals, with shorter gestation periods, will mate in early spring. Birds also mate in the spring because they lay their eggs only a few weeks after fertilisation. As with plants, the mechanisms are not fully understood. Nevertheless they are of interest and it is now known that human behaviour can be influenced by changes to the photoperiod.

Physiological homeostasis

Physiology is the study of the processes which take place in organisms.
Homeostasis is the maintenance of the steady state.

The need for homeostasis arises particularly from the sensitivity of enzymes to substrate concentration, temperature and pH changes. So it is in an organism's interest to have a fairly stable internal and external environment if at all possible. Many of the homeostatic processes involve **negative feedback** mechanisms.

Negative feedback is the process by which an increase in a factor triggers a mechanism which results in its decrease, and vice versa. By this method, many of the processes taking place in the body, and the concentrations of substances, are maintained at a constant level.

The **kidney** and the **liver** are both homeostatic organs. The kidney **osmoregulates**, i.e. it maintains the concentration of salts and the water content of the body at a fairly constant level. The liver is involved in many homeostatic processes including the maintenance of blood sugar level.

At the base of the brain is a small organ called the **hypothalamus**. It is connected intimately to the **pituitary gland** and has a myriad of functions, one of which is to monitor the osmotic concentration of the blood. If the blood becomes too concentrated (i.e. when you are thirsty) it stimulates the pituitary gland to produce **anti-diuretic hormone** (**ADH**). ADH is carried in the blood to the kidneys and there it stimulates them to reabsorb water from the urine. Reabsorption of water takes place in the collecting ducts (see page 38) of the kidney. As a consequence, the volume of urine is reduced and it becomes more concentrated. The hypothalamus then detects the dilution of the blood by water and the production of ADH is reduced. This is an example of **negative feedback control**.

Insulin and **glucagon** are hormones produced by the pancreas which influence glucose concentrations in the blood. The blood normally has around one gram of glucose per litre. Glucose is stored as **glycogen** in the liver and in the muscles. Glycogen is insoluble, so has no osmotic effect. When glucose is required by the body, glucagon stimulates the conversion of glycogen to glucose. **Adrenaline**, produced by the adrenal gland in times of fear or stress, also promotes the release of glucose from glycogen stores. Insulin has the opposite effect: it promotes the uptake of glucose by many cells, and the subsequent conversion of glucose to glycogen, particularly in liver and muscle cells.

The glands which produce hormones are called collectively **endocrine glands**.

Maintaining a constant temperature

It is in the interests of all animals to maintain a fairly constant temperature so that enzymes can operate under optimum conditions.

Animals are divided into **two** groups according to the way in which they maintain temperature.
Endotherms (birds and mammals) derive most of their body heat from their own metabolism and maintain a remarkably constant temperature. They are often called 'warm-blooded' animals.
Ectotherms (all other animals) derive most of their body heat from their surroundings and as a consequence their body temperature follows that of their surroundings. They are often called 'cold-blooded' animals.

In humans, the temperature of the blood is monitored by the **hypothalamus**. When body temperature rises significantly above 37°C various mechanisms are brought into play to reduce temperature. Sweating results in the evaporation of water from the skin and this takes heat energy from the body. The widening of tiny arteries (**vasodilation**), to allow more blood to flow near the surface of the skin, helps heat to escape more easily. Conversely, shivering and **vasoconstriction** help generate and conserve heat respectively. In the long term, the body's metabolic rate can also change to generate more, or less, heat. These mechanisms however, are not under conscious control. We can consciously help maintain a steady temperature, for example, by seeking shelter, changing our clothes, curling up in a ball or stretching out.

Section through human skin

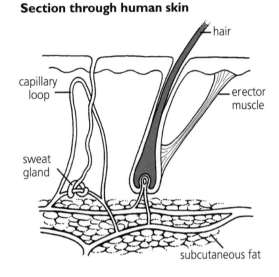

Other mammals can also control temperature in different ways.
• Dogs pant to increase evaporation of water from their lungs.
• Elephants have large ears which lose heat rapidly because their ears are thin and have large surface areas.
• Marine mammals have extra layers of blubber (fat) which insulate them from the cold.
• Desert rats live underground during the heat of the day.
• Many mammals can raise their hair using hair erector muscles (see diagram above). This traps more air, which is an excellent heat insulator. Our hair erector muscles still operate in the same way, but all we are left with is goose-pimples!

Marine iguana of the Galapagos islands

Some ectothermic animals have no need to control their body temperature because they live in an environment which hardly changes, e.g. animals which live in the sea or in tropical forest. Others can control their temperature remarkably effectively by behavioural means. For example, the Galapagos iguanas, like many reptiles, will warm up their bodies by basking in the heat of the sun, before diving into the sea to graze on algae.

Population dynamics

One of Darwin's observations about populations of organisms was their great capacity to increase in number. From the very simplest, to the most complex like ourselves, each species is capable of increasing its population size considerably. A doubling in numbers e.g. every hour, as in bacteria, is described as **exponential growth**.

Of course, such unchecked growth cannot continue. The world and universe would very quickly be overrun by bacteria (and humans) if it did. Disease, lack of food and predation all combine to hold populations in check and a balance is often achieved, based on what the environment can support. This is referred to as the **carrying capacity** of the environment. This will vary from month to month and year to year according to local variations in climate, food availability, numbers of predators and prevalence of disease.

The graph opposite shows the changes in population of sheep after they were introduced to Tasmania many years ago.

Notice that in the 'stationary phase' the actual numbers do not remain constant from year to year, but fluctuate about a 'set point'. That set point is the carrying capacity of the environment.

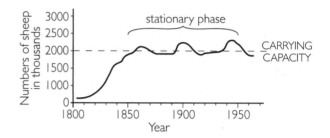

The factors which hold populations in check are often divided into two categories: those which vary with the size of the population – **density-dependent** factors – and those which are unaffected by the size of the population – **density-independent** factors. For example, a severe winter will reduce the number of garden birds, because many will simply die of cold. This will happen whether there are ten birds in a garden or one. Here, temperature would be a density-independent factor. Similarly, a heavy fall of snow will prevent the birds from finding food and all will die, regardless of the numbers present. However, if there are too many birds in a particular area, there may not be enough food for them or disease may spread from one to another more easily. Here, disease and the availability of food would be density-dependent factors.

Emigration and **immigration** can also affect the size of a local population, but in terms of the world population we can ignore immigration and emigration because space travel is too expensive, and at present we have nowhere to go anyway!

Currently, the human population is growing by almost 2% per annum. This may not sound a great deal, but equates to an *additional* three humans per second on this planet. At this rate, there will only be one square metre of land space for each human by the year 2500. Clearly, this cannot happen; the carrying capacity of the planet will be reached long before that date. However, the solution is very simple. Either we increase the death rate or reduce the birth rate. Of course, anyone suggesting we control the human population by leaving the birth rate alone and increasing the death rate is likely to be called a mass murderer or fascist. However, any mention of controlling human population in the other way, by regulating births, is also regarded by many as an unacceptable infringement of human rights. Like it or not, the human population explosion is now the Earth's most significant biological phenomenon. As a species of six billion individuals we require vast quantities of raw materials, and immense areas of land to grow crops and build roads and cities. In doing so we destroy the environment for many other species and now threaten to make it unfit for ourselves.

Saving the environment

Of course, many people recognise the dangers which result from the destruction of the Earth's natural ecosystems and the extinction of species, and governments have legislated to protect natural habitats and the species living in them. However, to do this effectively, there is a need to **monitor** wild populations and to understand how ecosystems can recover from damage.

Many agree that populations of animals and plants must be protected for a variety of reasons:
• they are aesthetically attractive
• there is a moral or religious obligation to do so
• there are many undiscovered sources of raw materials for foodstuffs and medicines
• there are undiscovered genes which can be used in genetic engineering to create new and useful products.

Consequently, it is important that populations of animals and plants are monitored carefully to ensure that, for example:
• there are sufficient, sustainable numbers to provide us with food and raw materials
• none are in danger of extinction
• pest species are kept under control
• levels of pollution can be checked using indicator species.

Succession

Where habitats have been devastated it is possible for them to recover. Communities can recover from natural phenomena such as flooding, drought or fire, so it is not surprising they can also recover from human damage. The colonisation of barren ground by plants and animals and the changes which follow is called an ecological **succession**. The changes which occur result from changes to the environment brought about by each succeeding community. For example, there is often an increase in the quality of soil as succession takes place.

An ecological succession

In a temperate ecosystem, the first plants to colonise bare ground to form a **pioneer community** are often lichens and mosses. These are then followed by small flowering plants, such as grasses. Later, larger flowering plants, bushes and sometimes trees will eventually follow, until the ground is covered by a mature evergreen or deciduous forest. This final stable mature community is called a **climax community**. Climax communities tend to have complex food webs, high biodiversity and high biomass.

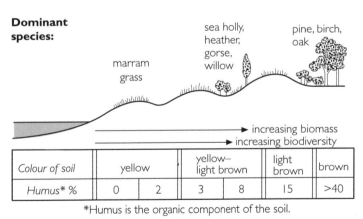

Colour of soil	yellow		yellow–light brown		light brown	brown
Humus* %	0	2	3	8	15	>40

*Humus is the organic component of the soil.

So if we have the will, it is possible to reverse the human devastation of the Earth's natural ecosystems. The habitats and the animals and plants which live in them are enormously resilient and have great capacity to recover from damage. The future of this planet lies unquestionably in our hands.

ANSWERS TO QUESTIONS

Page 6
approximately 10 μm (micrometres or microns)

Page 10
The R_f value is approximately 0·6.

Page 23
9 round yellow, 3 round green, 3 wrinkled yellow and 1 wrinkled green

Page 25

B   D   A   C genes

chromosome   (or mirror image)

Page 28
black mustard × cabbage → Abyssinian mustard
black mustard × turnip → brown mustard

Page 48
Graph 1 shows that as group size increases, individual ostriches spend more time with their heads down.
Graph 2 shows that as group size increases, there is an overall increase in the group's vigilance.

Page 55
10^{-8}M IAA promotes stem growth and inhibits root growth.
10^{-3}M IAA has no effect on growth of flowers and promotes stem growth.

Now that you have read this book, you might like to read its companion question book, written by the same author. *Questions in Higher Biology* contains around 300 questions, with answers. It also contains a simplified syllabus summary and a glossary of all the technical words you are likely to come across in the unit tests (NABs) and SQA examination.